Vocabulary Workshop

Level Green

Enriched Edition

with iWords Audio Program

Jerry L. Johns, Ph.D.
Senior Reading Consultant

Distinguished Teaching Professor Emeritus
Department of Literacy Education
Northern Illinois University

Consultants

Joseph Czarnecki, Ph.D.
Faculty Associate, School of Education
Johns Hopkins University
Baltimore, MD

Lucy Lugones
Technology Consultant
St. Luke's School
New York, NY

Christine Gialamas-Antonucci
Reading Specialist
Chicago Public Schools
Chicago, IL

Helen Wood Turner, Ed.D.
Reading Specialist
Turning Point Academy
Lanham, MD

 Sadlier

Vocabulary Workshop

Enriched Edition

with iWords Audio Program

Advisers

The publisher wishes to thank the following teachers and administrators, who read portions of the series prior to publication, for their comments and suggestions.

Carolyn Branch
Lead Charter Administrator
Kansas City, MO

Khawla Asmar
Assistant Principal
Milwaukee, WI

Amy Cristina
Teacher
Panama City, FL

Tara M. Gaiss
Literacy Specialist
Kings Park, NY

Ann Jennings
English Specialist
Rustburg, VA

Cora M. Kirby
Reading Specialist
Washington, DC

Lisa Mayer
Teacher
Houston, TX

Megan Mayfield
Teacher
Woodstock, GA

Julie Cambonga
Assistant Principal/Teacher
Sierra Madre, CA

Nancy Wahl
Elementary School Teacher
New York, NY

Photo Credits: Cover: pencil: Used under license from Shutterstock.com/Pedro Nogueira; wood grain on pencil: Used under license from Shutterstock.com/Christophe Testi. Interior: Alamy/Avico Ltd: 80 *top*; bobo: 96 *right*; Catchlight Visual Services/Denise Hager: 18 *bottom*; Geoff A. Howard: 79 *background*; Mooch Images Ltd: 79 *bottom right*; nobleIMAGES/David Noble: 153 *top*; Alex Segre: 18 *top*; VStock: 120. Artville: 171. The Bridgeman Art Library/Victoria & Albert Museum, London, UK/Illustration to 'The Princess and the Pea,' by Hans Christian Andersen, c.1911 by Edmund Dulac (1882-1953). Corbis/Pavalla Bagla: 110 *bottom*; Bettmann: 140, 141, 153 *bottom*; Flame/Tim Pannell: 27 *bottom left*; Kevin Fleming: 49; Todd Gipstein: 26; Historical: 143; Layne Kennedy: 100; T.E. Marr: 69 *top*; Owaki-Kulla: 16 *left*; Josef Scaylea: 133 *bottom*; Science Faction/Stephen Frink: 151 *inset*; Terra/Bob Krist: 69 *bottom*; zefa/Theo Allofs: 17 *right*. Dennis Cox/ChinaStock/Liu Liqun: 78 *bottom left*. Dreamstime/Icefields: 130; Ivo13: 183; Kingjon: 68. Fotosearch/Iconotec: 142. Getty Images/AFP: 182; Brand X Pictures: 27 *top*; The Christian Science Monitor/Melanie Stetson Freeman: 34; Digital Vision: 91; Getty Images Sport/Cameron Spencer: 131 *top*; Hulton Archive: 163; LOOK/Florian Werner: 121; Photodisc: 64 *left*, 180, 181; Stone/John E. Kelly: 80 *bottom*; Stone/Jean-Marc Truchet: 71; Taxi/Joel-Noel Reichel: 29 *top*; Workbook Stock/Scott Quinn Photography: 16 *center left*. The Granger Collection, New York: 64 *right*. The Image Works/Suzanne Dunn: 172; David Lassman: 90; Lee Snider: 133 *top*. iStockphoto/45RPM: 78 *bottom right*, 79 *bottom left*; craigrobinsonphoto: 9; HultonArchive: 180 *right*; jonpic: 171 *background*; magicinfoto: 26–27 *background*; protocolmedia: 88 *left*; Stuartb: 118; vasiliki: 131 *bottom*; zts: 119. Levi Strauss & Co. Archives: 96 *left*. Mary Evans/Classic Stock/C.P. Cushing: 181 *right*. Minden Pictures/NPL/Stephen Dalton: 29 *bottom*. NASA: 46, 47. National Geographic Stock: 109; Jon Foster: 108 *bottom*. National Historic Route 66 Federation: 16 *background inset*, 17 *left*. North Wind Archives: 180 *left*. Photolibrary/age fotostock/J.D. Dallet: 56–57 *background*; Blend Images/Karin Dreyer: 27 *bottom right*; Cultura RM/Yellowdog: 58 *top*; Imagebroker/Christian Heinrich: 170–171 *bottom*; Imagebroker/Martin Moxter: 110 *top*; Lineair/Ron Gilling: 8; LOOK-foto/Don Fuchs: 150–151 *background*; Rubberball: 162. Photo Researchers, Inc./Jerry Schad: 48. Punchstock/Blend Images: 70; Brand X Pictures: 101; photosindia: 89 *bottom*; Rubberball: 39 *bottom*. Used under license from Shutterstock.com/Blinka: 27 *center right*; DG Jervis: 58 *bottom*; Dr_Flash: 16 *background*; J. Helgason: 181 *left*; JinYoung Lee: 118 *background*; pirita: 173; Ronald Summers: 88 *right*, 88 *top*; Magdalena Szachowska: 39 *top*; Christophe Testi: 88 *bottom*; Tihis: 99 *bottom*. Amy Toensing: 108–109. SuperStock/Robert Harding Picture Library: 57. Visuals Unlimited, Inc./Brandon Cole: 158.

Illustrators: Scott Angle: 160–161. Janet Broxon: 36–37. Mike Gordon: 6–7. Tim Haggerty: 9, 10, 38, 40, 90, 92, 143,144. Martin Lemelman: 19, 20, 42, 49, 50, 74, 101, 102 124, 126, 156, 163, 188. Bob Ostrom: 22, 59, 60, 111, 112, 183, 184. Zina Saunders: 32, 52, 71, 72, 84 *top*, 94, 120, 122, 136, 152, 154, 164. Daryl Stevens: 62, 104, 114, 136, 146, 166, 176, 186. Chris Vallo: 12, 28, 30, 81, 82, 132, 134, 173, 174.

For additional online resources, go to **vocabularyworkshop.com** and enter the Student Access Code VWL11S9FBQT4.

S is a registered trademark of William H. Sadlier, Inc.

Printed in the United States of America.
ISBN: 978-0-8215-8003-5
23456789 BRR 14 13 12 11

Note to the Student

Most of the vocabulary words in **Level Green** will be new to you. Some words you may recognize. Others you may not know at all. The words have been chosen because they are words you will come across often. You will see them in schoolbooks and on tests. You will see them in books and magazines, as well as on the Internet. You will also hear them spoken by teachers and others in a variety of professions.

In each of the 18 units, you will read a passage that contains the 10 unit words. You will see and hear how the words are used in the passage. Then you will learn more about them, including their definitions, pronunciations, parts of speech, and how they are used in sentences. You will also find synonyms and antonyms for the words. As you complete the pages in the unit, not only will you practice using the words, but you will also show what you know about them.

Each unit also helps you build vocabulary beyond the unit words. For example, in **Word Study**, you will learn how to use word parts (prefixes, suffixes, roots) to figure out the meanings of unfamiliar words. In **Shades of Meaning**, you will learn some phrases that have special meanings. You will also learn some idioms.

When you have finished this book, your vocabulary will have grown. All the words you have learned will be part of your personal vocabulary, helping you to become a better reader, writer, and speaker.

Interactive Online Activities

Don't forget to look at the online activities that extend and enrich the instruction and practice contained in **Level Green**. Access to these free activities and more is available at vocabularyworkshop.com.

Contents

Introducing the Words

Read the following fable about how a hungry fox tries to get food. Notice how the highlighted words are used. These are the words you will be learning in this unit.

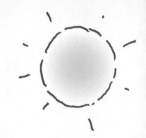

The Fox and the Grapes

(an Aesop Fable)

On a hot summer afternoon, a fox became quite hungry and thirsty. Eagerly, he began to search for his next meal. He looked up and spotted a vine of grapes hanging from a tall tree. As he stared at the juicy fruit, his mouth watered. These grapes were not the common, small green grapes he usually found. Each one was as big as a red plum.

"Ah!" he said. "Red grapes! I truly prefer the red grapes to the green ones! The red grapes are so much sweeter."

He stood up on his back legs and sniffed the grapes. Then he tried to pull them down. Unfortunately, that didn't work. The fox scratched his head and wondered what he should do next. Climbing the tree was out of the question. Still, the grapes were too high to allow him to reach them. He would have to use his strong legs to leap up and snatch a bunch.

He walked back several yards and then ran toward the grapes. He pumped his legs and jumped up with all the force he could gather, but he missed the vine. Instead, he tumbled into a nearby mud puddle.

Now the fox was hungrier than ever. His stomach rumbled like a freight train. He said, "I must try again!"

He walked back twenty yards this time. Then he ran faster toward his goal—the bunch of ripe, juicy grapes. Alas, his second try was no better than the first. He hit his head on the firm ground and then rolled head over heels. He sat on a tree stump and rubbed his head. Hitting the ground like that had given him a horrible headache.

Listen to this passage at
vocabularyworkshop.com.

This particular fox had never been a patient creature, and now his hunger was making him anxious and grumpy. He had to get those grapes.

The fox stood up once more, but his legs were unsteady. He wobbled backward and felt a little faint. He sat on the ground until he felt stronger. Finally, there was only a trace of a headache left.

He walked back fifty yards this time. Then he ran full speed ahead. He jumped up, but he missed the grapes and fell into a patch of thorny bushes.

"Ouch!" the fox yelled.

He pulled himself out of the patch. Twigs with thorns tore at his fur, and he howled with each step he took. Then he shook his fist at the grapes.

He yelled, "What a dumb bunch of grapes! Let someone else eat you. I bet you're bitter anyway!"

And with that, he walked away in a huff.

Moral: *It is easier to pretend you do not want what you cannot get.*

Definitions

You were introduced to the words below in the passage on pages 6–7. Study the spelling, pronunciation, part of speech, and definition of each word. Write the word on the line in the sentence. Then read the synonyms and antonyms.

1. allow
(ə laů')

(v.) to let do or happen; to agree

My parents ___allow___ me to ride my bike in good weather.

SYNONYM: permit
ANTONYMS: forbid, prevent

2. bitter
(bit' ər)

(adj.) sharp and unpleasant; angry or hurt

The unripe fruit tasted ___bitter___.

SYNONYM: harsh
ANTONYMS: sweet, mild

3. common
(käm' ən)

(adj.) found often; average

A cat is a ___common___ pet.

SYNONYMS: familiar, ordinary
ANTONYMS: unusual, odd

4. faint
(fānt)

(v.) to pass out

The hot sun made the dancer ___faint___ on stage.

(adj.) not clear; weak

The writing was so ___faint___ that I had trouble reading it.

SYNONYMS: (adj.) unclear, slight, faded
ANTONYMS: (adj.) clear, strong

5. firm
(fûrm)

(adj.) solid; steady or strong

The climber kept a ___firm___ grip on the rope.

(n.) a business or small company

My mother works at a law ___firm___.

SYNONYM: (adj.) hard
ANTONYMS: (adj.) soft; weak

6. force
(fôrs)

(n.) strength; power

The ___*force*___ of the wind knocked over the tree.

(v.) to cause to do something by using strength or power

Firefighters must sometimes ___*force*___ *their way into a burning building.*

SYNONYMS: (n.) might; (v.) make, push
ANTONYM: (n.) weakness

7. goal
(gōl)

(n.) something a person wants and works for; the area into which players must move a ball or puck in order to score in some sports

My ___*goal*___ *in life is to become a scientist.*

SYNONYMS: (n.) target, aim, plan

8. patient
(pā′ shənt)

(n.) a person getting medical care

The ___*patient*___ *had to stay in the hospital.*

(adj.) able to stay calm when faced with pain, trouble, or a long wait

My teacher was ___*patient*___ *as I learned the new song.*

ANTONYMS: (adj.) impatient, anxious

9. prefer
(pri fûr′)

(v.) to like better than others; to tend to choose

I ___*prefer*___ *summer to winter.*

10. trace
(trās)

(n.) a small amount left behind showing that something was there

The air had only a ___*trace*___ *of smoke after the fire.*

(v.) to copy by following over the lines of something as seen through a sheet of paper

If you want to copy a design, you can ___*trace*___ *it.*

SYNONYMS: (n.) mark, sign, track; (v.) outline

Match the Meaning

vocabularyworkshop.com
Practice unit words with interactive games and activities.

Choose the word whose meaning is suggested by the clue given.
Then write the word on the line provided.

1. If you __prefer__ tacos to pizza, you like tacos better.
   a. force   b. prefer   c. trace

2. A soccer field has a __goal__ on each end.
   a. goal   b. trace   c. patient

3. When many people have the same name, the name is
   __common__.
   a. common   b. faint   c. firm

4. If your parents __allow__ you to stay up
   late, they give you permission to do so.
   a. trace   b. force   c. allow

5. A __bitter__ person may feel angry because
   of a bad experience.
   a. firm   b. bitter   c. common

6. To be __patient__ is to be calm and
   understanding.
   a. bitter   b. faint   c. patient

7. __Faint__ pencil marks are light and
   difficult to see.
   a. Faint   b. Patient   c. Firm

8. If you __force__ open a box, you use your
   strength to get inside it.
   a. force   b. faint   c. trace

The soccer player kicked the ball into the **goal**.

9. About twenty-five people work at the __firm__.
   a. firm   b. goal   c. patient

10. When you __trace__ a design, you draw over its lines on
    another sheet of paper.
    a. allow   b. trace   c. prefer

Synonyms

Choose the word that is most nearly the **same** in meaning as the word or phrase in **dark print.** Then write your choice on the line provided.

1. the **strength** of the wind
   a. force   b. goal   c. patient

   force

2. **like** dogs **more than** cats
   a. allow   b. prefer   c. force

   prefer

3. **outline** a shape
   a. allow   b. force   c. trace

   trace

4. a **dim** light
   a. bitter   b. common   c. faint

   faint

5. a coach who is **understanding**
   a. patient   b. firm   c. bitter

   patient

6. with a **plan** of finishing early
   a. trace   b. firm   c. goal

   goal

Antonyms

Choose the word that is most nearly **opposite** in meaning to the word or phrase in **dark print.** Then write your choice on the line provided.

1. a **weak** handshake
   a. patient   b. firm   c. faint

   firm

2. **forbid** a change in plans
   a. trace   b. prefer   c. allow

   allow

3. an **unusual** insect
   a. common   b. faint   c. firm

   common

4. a **sweet** fruit
   a. bitter   b. patient   c. common

   bitter

Completing the Sentence

Choose the word from the box that best completes each item below. Then write the word on the line provided. (You may have to change the word's ending.)

~~allow~~	~~bitter~~	~~common~~
~~faint~~	~~firm~~	~~force~~
~~goal~~	~~patient~~	
~~prefer~~	~~trace~~	

The Broken Arm

- It was a great day for a soccer game. I took my position in the __goal__.

- A player ran toward me with great __force__.

- I did not want to __allow__ anyone to score.

- She gave the ball a __firm__ kick with her right foot.

- I stopped the ball, but I heard a cracking sound in my arm. The pain was so bad that I thought I was going to __faint__.

- Soon I was at the hospital. I went from being a player to being a __patient__.

Spinach Power

- Many people think spinach is too __bitter__, but I think it is delicious!

- Some people __prefer__ to eat spinach raw in a salad. Others like cooked spinach.

- It is __common__ to cook spinach with eggs.

- I like spinach steamed with a __trace__ of garlic.

Word Associations

Circle the letter next to the choice that best completes the sentence or answers the question. Pay special attention to the word in dark print.

1. What can make you **bitter**?
   a. winning a prize
   b. riding a bike
   c. visiting a friend
   d. losing a race

2. If you **prefer** milk to water, you
   a. would rather drink water.
   b. would rather drink milk.
   c. think milk tastes bad.
   d. don't like milk.

3. A **faint** light is
   a. strong.
   b. very bright.
   c. easy to see.
   d. hard to see.

4. If you **trace** your hand, you
   a. outline it.
   b. color on it.
   c. shake it.
   d. slap it.

5. What may your parents say if they **allow** you to do something?
   a. "It's okay with us."
   b. "You're not old enough."
   c. "We don't think that's a good idea."
   d. "Maybe some other time."

6. Which of these has a strong **force**?
   a. a breeze
   b. a feather
   c. a hurricane
   d. a snow flurry

7. A **patient** person probably
   a. yells a lot.
   b. never feels calm.
   c. doesn't complain too much.
   d. can't sit still.

8. Which of these is **firm**?
   a. a flower
   b. water
   c. mud
   d. frozen ground

9. A **common** mistake is a mistake that
   a. few people make.
   b. is very dangerous.
   c. many people have made before.
   d. has been made for the first time.

10. If your sister met her **goal**, she might say,
    a. "I did it!"
    b. "I can't read these two books by tomorrow."
    c. "I think I can do it."
    d. "I wish I hadn't done that."

Word Study • Dictionary: Multiple-Meaning Words

A **multiple-meaning word** is a word with more than one meaning. One example from this unit is *goal* (page 9). If you look up *goal* in a dictionary, you will find an entry with numbers showing the word's different meanings.

> **goal 1.** something a person wants and works for: *It is my goal to read five books.* **2.** the area into which players must move a ball or puck in order to score in some sports: *A hockey goal is four feet high.*

Read this sentence: *I ran toward the soccer goal.* You can tell from the dictionary entries for *goal* that this sentence uses meaning 2 of *goal*.

Look at the chart to find other examples of multiple-meaning words.

bound	1. to leap; spring 2. held together by ties
store	1. a place where things are sold 2. to gather and keep for future use
tire	1. to use up strength or energy 2. a rubber covering that fits around a wheel

PRACTICE *Write the word from the chart above that best completes each sentence. Then write the number of the meaning.*

1 **1.** The robber was _____tired_____ by his hands.

1 **2.** I took a nap so I wouldn't _____tired_____ easily.

2 **3.** A cactus plant can _____store_____ water in its stem.

1 **4.** We watched the deer _____bound_____ across the lawn.

APPLY *Write a sentence for each word below. Be sure the sentence shows one of the meanings in the chart.*

5. bound ___I bounded in the bounce house.___

6. store ___I went to the store.___

7. tire ___I went to the tire shop.___

Speak *Think of two meanings for each word below. Then use one of the words in a sentence. Ask your partner to tell what the word means.*

bat   **fly**

Shades of Meaning • Words That Describe How Things Taste

In the passage "The Fox and the Grapes" on pages 6–7, you read this sentence: *I bet you're* **bitter** *anyway!* In the sentence, the fox is describing how he thinks the grapes taste. *Bitter* means the opposite of *sweet*. Both *bitter* and *sweet* describe how things taste.

Look at the words in the chart. Learning the words will help you choose the right word to use when you describe how things taste.

bitter	Foods that taste **bitter** have a sharp or unpleasant taste.
bland	Foods that are **bland** are mild and without a strong flavor.
spicy	**Spicy** foods have a strong flavor because they are made with spices, such as hot pepper.

PRACTICE *Write the name of each food under the word that best describes it.*

bread   chili   cranberry   grapefruit   lime
potato   salsa   sausage   white rice

bitter	bland	spicy
1. lime	4. bread	7. chili
2. grapefruit	5. potato	8. salsa
3. cranberry	6. white rice	9. sausage

APPLY *Use* **bitter**, **bland**, *or* **spicy** *to complete each sentence so that it makes sense.*

10. I had to drink lots of water after ___spicy___ .

11. I knew it was a grapefruit because ___bitter___ .

12. When I felt sick, I could only eat ___bland___ .

Introducing the Words

Read the following magazine article about a famous American highway. Notice how the highlighted words are used. These are the words you will be learning in this unit.

Driving on Route 66
(Magazine Article)

Most likely, the street you live on is smooth and paved, not rough and dusty. But are you aware that paved roads were not always so common? About a hundred years ago, if you wanted to travel, your horse and buggy would use a dirt road. Sometimes, these roads were little more than trails. Their paths drifted this way and that.

In 1908, the Model T Ford was introduced to Americans. This was the first car that people could afford to buy. However, roads that were made for horses weren't good enough for cars. A car had a solid body, and it weighed a lot. It could get stuck when it was driven on a muddy road. An entire trip could be ruined.

In 1916, Congress set aside money to build roads. Later, a paved route that started in chilly Chicago was mapped out. It would go through Oklahoma and end in warm, sunny Los Angeles. The road was named Route 66. In 1938, the last section of the road was paved.

Route 66 was a popular highway. Many people were tired of long, cold winters. Their aim was to move to a place with mild weather. They used Route 66 to travel west. Truckers carrying goods used Route 66, too. Motels and restaurants popped up along the highway.

Over the next thirty years, many people used Route 66. It was nicknamed "Main Street of America." There was even a popular television show called *Route 66*.

Then came much bigger highways that crossed the country. People were buying newer and faster cars. They wanted better roads and more lanes. By the 1980s, these big highways were in place. That was the beginning of the end for Route 66.

Today, Route 66 is no longer a main route westward, but it refuses to disappear. Drivers traveling west on other roads might take a side trip and travel along Route 66. Once there, they might pause at the stores and motels that are still open. There won't be many, though, because many towns have disappeared. Many buildings are empty, and people have moved away.

Route 66 is a story of both success and defeat. It was an important road for many years, but then its importance faded. Many people still seek out Route 66 to discover what life on the highway once was like.

In the early days, people often traveled together.

Definitions

You were introduced to the words below in the passage on pages 16–17. Study the spelling, pronunciation, part of speech, and definition of each word. Write the word on the line in the sentence. Then read the synonyms and antonyms.

1. aim
(ām)

(v.) to point or direct at a target

In archery, you should __aim__ for the center of the target.

(n.) a purpose or goal

My __aim__ was to win the state spelling bee.

SYNONYMS: (v. & n.) plan, target

2. aware
(ə wâr')

(adj.) knowing or realizing

We were __aware__ that it was getting late.

SYNONYM: knowledgeable

3. defeat
(di fēt')

(v.) to beat in a game or battle

The Tigers hoped to __defeat__ the Bears in the last game.

(n.) loss; failure

The __defeat__ was difficult for the player because she had worked so hard.

SYNONYMS: (v.) conquer, overcome; (n.) downfall
ANTONYM: (n.) win

4. drift
(drift)

(v.) to be carried away by water or air

The balloon began to __drift__ away from the child.

SYNONYMS: float; wander, stray

5. mild
(mīld)

(adj.) gentle, not harsh

The doctor spoke to the young child in a _____mild_____ tone of voice.

SYNONYMS: calm; warm; ANTONYM: strong

---

6. pause
(pôz)

(v.) to stop for a short time

Let's _____pause_____ to think about what happened.

(n.) a short stop

There was a _____pause_____ between two scenes in the play.

SYNONYMS: (v.) halt; (n.) break
ANTONYMS: (v.) continue, proceed

---

7. refuse
(ri fyüz')

(v.) to not accept or agree to something

I _____refuse_____ to admit that I was wrong.

SYNONYMS: deny, reject
ANTONYMS: accept, agree

---

8. route
(rüt) or (raůt)

(n.) a road or way of travel between two places

My bus takes the quickest _____route_____ to school.

SYNONYMS: path, course

---

9. ruin
(rü' in)

(v.) to destroy or damage something

Big waves will _____ruin_____ my sand castle.

SYNONYMS: break, wreck, spoil
ANTONYMS: save, fix, restore

---

10. solid
(sä' lid)

(adj.) having shape and hardness; not liquid or gas; very strong and reliable

After the boat ride, I was happy to be back on _____solid_____ ground.

SYNONYMS: hard, firm; ANTONYMS: weak, flimsy

Match the Meaning

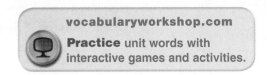

Choose the word whose meaning is suggested by the clue given.
Then write the word on the line provided.

1. To __ruin__ a house is to destroy it.
   a. ruin   b. aim   c. drift

2. A __route__ is a path from one place to another.
   a. pause   b. defeat   c. route

3. When you __pause__ a video, you stop it
   for a little while.
   a. aim   b. ruin   c. pause

4. To __drift__ is to float away.
   a. pause   b. drift   c. defeat

5. __mild__ weather is warm and pleasant.
   a. Aware   b. Solid   c. Mild

6. When you shoot a basketball, you should
   __aim__ for the hoop.
   a. refuse   b. aim   c. pause

7. Ice is the __solid__ form of water.
   a. solid   b. aware   c. mild

8. If you are __aware__ of the danger, you
   know about it.
   a. mild   b. solid   c. aware

9. When you __defeat__ someone in checkers,
   you win the game.
   a. aim   b. defeat   c. refuse

10. If you __refuse__ to answer a question,
    you do not answer it.
    a. refuse   b. defeat   c. pause

The artist carved a toy from
a solid block of wood.

Synonyms

Choose the word that is most nearly the **same** in meaning as the word or phrase in **dark print**. Then write your choice on the line provided.

1. beat the other team
a. refuse   b. defeat   c. drift   _____

2. point at the target
a. drift   b. aim   c. refuse   _____

3. take a new **way**
a. route   b. pause   c. defeat   _____

4. a **strong and thick** door
a. solid   b. mild   c. aware   _____

5. wander away from the group
a. drift   b. ruin   c. defeat   _____

Antonyms

Choose the word that is most nearly **opposite** in meaning to the word or phrase in **dark print**. Then write your choice on the line provided.

1. accept the invitation
a. aim   b. defeat   c. refuse   _____

2. fix a drawing
a. pause   b. ruin   c. aim   _____

3. a **cold** winter
a. mild   b. solid   c. aware   _____

4. continue the game
a. pause   b. aim   c. defeat   _____

5. not know that Dad was waiting
a. solid   b. aware   c. mild   _____

Completing the Sentence

Choose the word from the box that best completes each item below. Then write the word on the line provided. (You may have to change the word's ending.)

aim	aware	defeat
drift	mild	pause
refuse	route	
ruin	solid	

Body Boarding

■ During _____ weather at the beach, you might try body boarding.

■ Body boards look like small surfboards. They are usually made out of _____ foam.

■ Make sure the body board will not

_____ away if you fall off.

■ Wade out into the water until it reaches your waist.

When a good wave comes, _____ your board toward the shore and jump on.

■ Be _____ of other people around you, so you don't crash into them.

The Rainy Parade

■ If there's one thing that can

_____ a parade, it's rain.

■ Last summer, we _____ to let the weather stop us from going to the Fourth of July parade.

■ We grabbed our raincoats and umbrellas and found a great spot along

the parade _____.

■ As we watched, there were a few _____ in the rainfall.

■ We cheered for the soaking wet musicians and performers marching by.

We were so glad we didn't let the rain _____ us!

Word Associations

*Circle the letter next to the choice that best completes the sentence or answers the question. Pay special attention to the word in **dark print**.*

1. If you **refuse** to do something, you might say,
   a. "It would be my pleasure."
   b. "Can you help me with this?"
   c. "I'll never do that!"
   d. "I guess I could do it."

2. Which of these is **solid**?
   a. a bubble
   b. a rock
   c. a raindrop
   d. a cloud

3. If you **defeat** someone in a race, you might
   a. cheer.
   b. frown.
   c. be upset.
   d. complain.

4. To find a **route** to your friend's house, you can look
   a. in a dictionary.
   b. at a compass.
   c. at a map.
   d. in a science book.

5. If a team wants to **pause** a game, they might ask,
   a. "May we take a time-out?"
   b. "Which player scored?"
   c. "What's the score?"
   d. "How can we win?"

6. If your **aim** is to play in the band, you should
   a. practice your instrument.
   b. give up your instrument.
   c. watch TV all day.
   d. skip your music lessons.

7. What might **ruin** a good day?
   a. getting an A on a test
   b. scoring a goal in a game
   c. winning an art prize
   d. falling in a mud puddle

8. A dog with a **mild** manner might
   a. nip at you.
   b. sleep on your lap.
   c. bark all day.
   d. snap at the mail carrier.

9. If scientists are **aware** that a storm is coming, they
   a. don't know about it
   b. can stop it from happening.
   c. have no information about it.
   d. can warn people about it.

10. A boat in the lake may **drift** because
    a. it's near a lot of boats.
    b. it's not tied to the pier.
    c. it's late in the day.
    d. it's a calm day.

Word Study • Context Clues 1

When you read, you may come across words that you do not know. When this happens, look for **context clues** in the sentence to help you figure out the word's meaning. Sometimes, a sentence will give the definition of the word you do not know. Look at the example below.

Definition	*The short, sharp points on the stem of a rose are called* ***thorns***.
	The words ***short***, ***sharp points*** *tell what* ***thorns*** *means.*

PRACTICE *Read each sentence. Write the meaning of the word in* ***dark print*** *on the line.*

1. A **gust** is a sudden blast of wind. _____

2. She didn't want to **rumple**, or wrinkle, her new skirt. _____

3. He is a **pirate**, a person who robs people on ships. _____

4. A boat sails on the **surface**, or top part, of the ocean. _____

5. The children sat on the **stoop**, a small staircase that leads to the

   entrance of a house. _____

APPLY *Read each sentence. Underline the words that help you figure out the meaning of the word in* ***dark print***. *Then write a new sentence for the word to show that you understand its meaning.*

6. The four campers floated down the river on a wooden **raft**, a kind of flat boat.

   _____

7. We could hear the **lark**, a song bird, chirping in the early morning.

   _____

8. The **tutor**, a person who gives private lessons, helped me with my writing project.

   _____

 Choose a word from the dictionary. Make up a sentence using that word. Make sure your sentence provides good context clues. Ask your partner to figure out the meaning of the word.

Shades of Meaning • Literal and Nonliteral Meanings

In the passage "Driving on Route 66" on pages 16–17, you read that Route 66 was a popular highway for many years. Then faster cars were built, and drivers needed wider lanes for driving. These events helped to **drive home** the need for bigger highways. In this sentence, the phrase *drive home* has a special meaning. It means "to make a strong point."

Now read this sentence: *Yesterday, we had to **drive home** in the heavy rain.* In this sentence, the words *drive* and *home* have their dictionary meanings. Here, *drive home* has nothing to do with making a point about something.

Look at the words in the first column of the chart below. The words can be thought of as individual words or as phrases. The meanings, when used as words or as phrases, are given in the second column.

take steps	1. to move by foot 2. to take action in order to make something happen or to stop something
turned the corner	1. to change the direction you are moving by going around the place where two roads or walls meet 2. to get better after a difficult time
set aside	1. to place out of the way 2. to save for some reason

PRACTICE *Read each sentence. Look at the words in **dark print**. Decide which meaning from the chart above is shown. Write the number of the meaning on the line.*

_____ **1.** We **took steps** to protect our house from storm damage.

_____ **2.** We **set aside** our homework to set the table for dinner.

_____ **3.** She **took steps** slowly along the balance beam.

_____ **4.** I knew I had **turned the corner** when my fever went down.

_____ **5.** Each week, I **set aside** some of my allowance to help pay for camp.

_____ **6.** The runner **turned the corner** and raced to the finish line.

APPLY *Write a sentence to show one meaning of the words in **dark print**. Use those words in your sentence.*

7. take steps _____

8. turned the corner _____

Introducing the Words

Read the following magazine article about ways to help save natural resources. Notice how the highlighted words are used. These are the words you will be learning in this unit.

Going Green Every Day
(Magazine Article)

D o you want to help save the earth? You can, and it doesn't have to be a struggle. Doing little things every day can really help.

Do you recycle? Recycling helps save Earth's resources. Setting aside paper takes only a few moments, but it can save many trees. Many bottles and cans are returnable for money. You can get five cents or more when you return them to the store. Check the label of these containers to find their return value. Once recycled, paper, bottles, and cans can be used again.

Do you reuse items you already have? Can you bring your lunch in a paper bag? Every bag you use a second time doesn't cost you an extra penny. Now that's a bargain! Think of other items that you can reuse. Tell your family members about them. Listen to them gasp at your ideas.

Did you know that you can clean most of the things in your house with water, vinegar, and baking soda? Many people are sensitive to chemical cleaners. These products can cause allergies or skin problems. Baking soda and vinegar are not harmful, yet they can clean sinks, floors, and other big surfaces. These simple, natural cleaners cost less, too.

Water is a natural resource. When you brush your teeth, don't wander away and leave the water running. Turn it off. Reduce the amount of water you use. You will save two gallons or more. You can also reduce the amount of electricity you use by turning off the lights when you leave a room.

Be loyal to your local farmers' markets. Many fruits and vegetables are grown far away. They travel on ships and trucks to get to where you live. Farmers who sell their goods at the local farmers' market don't have to travel as far to bring you your food. Buying from them saves a lot of gas and oil.

Cleaning up your town on Earth Day is a great way to become active in your community. Most towns clear litter from parks, roads, and the banks of rivers on Earth Day. Next April, see what you can do to help!

Going green is as easy as taking a walk and enjoying the outdoors. Vary your walks to see something new each time. Watch a small animal and see where it goes. Nature is a never-ending show, and watching it requires no electricity!

Definitions

You were introduced to the words below in the passage on pages 26–27. Study the spelling, pronunciation, part of speech, and definition of each word. Write the word on the line in the sentence. Then read the synonyms and antonyms.

1. active
(ak′ tiv)

(adj.) taking action; full of movement
To be healthy, it is important to stay __active__.

SYNONYMS: lively, busy, energetic
ANTONYMS: slow, lazy, passive

2. bargain
(bär′ gən)

(n.) an agreement between two people or groups; something sold cheaply; a good deal

The baseball cards were a __bargain__ *at $1 a pack.*

(v.) to ask for a lower price; to agree to sell something for less

Not many store owners like to __bargain__ *with customers.*

SYNONYMS: (n.) "steal"; (v.) haggle

3. gasp
(gasp)

(v.) to breathe in quickly or have trouble breathing because of fear or shock; to catch one's breath

I'm sure you're going to __gasp__ *when you see the scary part of the movie.*

(n.) the act of gasping or panting

We heard the sound of a __gasp__ *as the runner crossed the finish line.*

SYNONYM: (v.) pant

4. loyal
(loi′ əl)

(adj.) faithful to one's country, a person, or an idea
The __loyal__ *soldier was proud to serve her country.*

ANTONYMS: unfaithful, treacherous

5. resource
(rē′ sôrs)

(n.) a source of useful supplies, materials, or information

An encyclopedia is a valuable __resource__.

SYNONYM: supply

6. sensitive
(sen′ sə tiv)

(adj.) reacting to something quickly; easily hurt or bothered

My teeth are _____sensitive_____ to cold drinks.

SYNONYMS: touchy, delicate
ANTONYMS: insensitive, uncaring

7. struggle
(strug′ əl)

(n.) an enormous effort or attempt; a battle

It was a _____struggle_____ to climb the mountain.

(v.) to try hard; to make a great effort; to fight

The father had to _____struggle_____ to win the tug-of-war.

SYNONYMS: (v.) strive, wrestle

8. value
(val′ yü)

(n.) something important; the worth of something; an amount

I did not know the _____value_____ of the painting.

(v.) to estimate the worth of; to think highly of

I _____value_____ your opinion because you are so wise.

SYNONYMS: (n.) importance; (v.) assess, price; treasure
ANTONYMS: (v.) scorn, reject

9. vary
(vâr′ ē)

(v.) to do in a new way; to make different; to change

To make lunch interesting, _____vary_____ your choice of vegetables.

SYNONYM: alter

10. wander
(wän′ dər)

(v.) to move around without a plan or goal; to get lost

Did you see the deer _____wander_____ into our backyard?

SYNONYMS: roam, ramble, stray
ANTONYMS: stay, remain

Match the Meaning

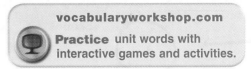
Choose the word whose meaning is suggested by the clue given.
Then write the word on the line provided.

1. To be _____loyal_____ to your country is to be faithful to it.
   a. active   (b. loyal)   c. sensitive

2. When you _____vary_____ your tasks, you change them.
   a. gasp   b. wander   (c. vary)

3. A source of useful materials is a _____resource_____
   (a. resource)   b. gasp   c. bargain

4. If you _____wander_____ off without thinking,
   you can get lost.
   a. gasp   b. struggle   (c. wander)

5. To _____gasp_____ is to take in a deep breath.
   a. bargain   (b. gasp)   c. vary

6. Soccer is a(n) _____active_____ sport because the
   players run a lot.
   a. loyal   b. sensitive   (c. active)

7. The worth of a car will tell you its _____value_____.
   a. struggle   b. resource   (c. value)

8. _____Sensitive_____ people can get their feelings
   hurt easily.
   (a. Sensitive)   b. Active   c. Loyal

9. When you _____bargain_____ for something,
   you often end up paying a lower price.
   a. vary   (b. bargain)   c. wander

10. To work at a new and difficult job can be a _____struggle_____.
    a. gasp   b. value   (c. struggle)

The noise of the
fireworks display caused
the girl to **gasp**.

Synonyms

Choose the word that is most nearly the **same** in meaning as the word or phrase in **dark print**. Then write your choice on the line provided.

1. hear the jogger **pant**
   a. bargain   b. wander   (c. gasp)   _gasp_

2. an **effort** to walk
   a. resource   b. value   (c. struggle)   _struggle_

3. a valuable **supply**
   a. bargain   (b. value)   c. resource   _value_

4. **roam** into the woods
   a. vary   b. bargain   (c. wander)   _wander_

5. **change** your direction
   (a. vary)   b. struggle   c. bargain   _vary_

6. **haggle** for a better price
   a. gasp   b. wander   (c. bargain)   _bargain_

Antonyms

Choose the word that is most nearly **opposite** in meaning to the word or phrase in **dark print**. Then write your choice on the line provided.

1. an **unfaithful** friend
   (a. loyal)   b. active   c. sensitive   _loyal_

2. a **slow** morning
   a. sensitive   (b. active)   c. loyal   _active_

3. an **uncaring** companion
   (a. sensitive)   b. loyal   c. active   _sensitive_

4. **reject** their advice
   a. bargain   b. vary   (c. value)   _value_

Completing the Sentence

Choose the word from the box that best completes each item below. Then write the word on the line provided. (You may have to change the word's ending.)

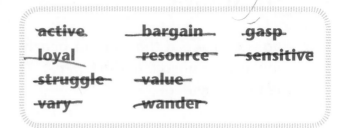

active   bargain   gasp
loyal   resource   sensitive
struggle   value
vary   wander

Tools

- Our neighbor is a carpenter. If you __wander__ into her garage, you will find many tools.

- She knows the __value__ of tools. She takes care of them so that they will last a long time.

- Our neighbor often buys paint. She is __loyal__ to her favorite brand of paint and won't buy any other kind. She is happy to find out that the price of paint in the new hardware store is a __bargain__. She used to pay much more for the same paint in other stores.

- Carpenters are physically __active__. They move around a lot while they work.

Seasons

- In the summer, the weather in the mountains can __vary__. It might be hot in the morning, rainy in the early afternoon, and cool in the evening.

- People with __sensitive__ skin can get bad sunburns in the summer if they don't wear sunscreen.

- Flowers bloom in the spring and summer. They need water, a natural __resource__, in order to grow.

- It can be a __struggle__ getting to school when there is a snowstorm. It's hard to walk or to drive.

- Your first breath of the icy air can make you __gasp__.

Word Study • Word Families

A **word family** is a group of related words that share a basic word part but that have different endings. The words *loyal* (page 28), *loyalty*, and *loyally* all belong to the same word family.

loyal	faithful to one's country, a person, or an idea
loyalty	the quality of being loyal
loyally	doing something in a loyal way

The words in a family share some meaning. If you know one word in a family, you can figure out the meanings of the other words.

PRACTICE *Read each sentence. Each word in* **dark print** *is related to a word in the box. Underline the related word that best completes each sentence.*

> act   care
> collect   company
> loyal

1. I wear a red cap to baseball games to show (action/**loyalty**) to the team.

2. Please walk (**carefully**/loyally) across the wet floor.

3. My favorite (collection/**actor**) is in a new movie.

4. My dog is my best (**companion**/loyalty) on walks through the park.

5. I started (**collecting**/acting) stamps when I was six years old.

6. The (**active**/careful) child would not sit quietly in her chair.

APPLY *Add the ending in parentheses ( ) to form a related word. Then write a sentence with the new word. The first one has been done for you.*

7. **teach** (**er**) = _____teacher_____

   Mr. Smith is a math teacher at the high school.

8. **friend** (**ly**) = _friendly_

   I will talk to everyone friendly.

9. **select** (**ed**) = _selected_

   My teacher selected me as a fine collecter.

✏️ **Write** *Choose two words from Units 1–3. Create a word family for each. Write the unit word. Then write all the related words you can think of. Use a dictionary to check spellings and meanings.*

Example: drift, drifts, drifted, drifting, drifter

Vocabulary for Comprehension

*Read the following passage in which some of the words you have studied in Units 1–3 appear in **dark print**. Then answer the questions on page 35.*

Monkey Business

The saying *monkey business* usually means "acting silly." However, there are some real-life monkeys that are in business. They are in the business of helping people. Helping Hands is the name of the group that offers this service. At Helping Hands, the **goal** is to teach monkeys how to aid people who cannot move parts of their bodies.

Helping Hands trains capuchin (ka pü′ shin) monkeys. Capuchins have great hand skills. This makes them a perfect fit for people who need help. Also, capuchins are very **active**. They enjoy having jobs to do.

When the monkeys are young, they are sent to live in a foster home. Here, they learn what it is like to live with people. After five to ten years, the monkeys go to Monkey College. At Monkey College, the monkeys learn how to do things that disabled people need help with. They learn how to turn on lights and get food from the refrigerator. They even learn how to work a DVD player. The monkeys can put in a disc, play it, and **pause** it. They can take out the disc when it is done. It can take three to four years for a monkey to learn all the skills. The trainers must be **patient**. They must show the monkeys what to do over and over.

Capuchin monkeys are trained to develop special skills to help people.

During the classes at Monkey College, trainers pay attention to what a monkey is good at. The **aim** is to place each monkey with a person whose needs best match the monkey's skills. Once a monkey is placed in a home, it will be a **loyal** friend and helper. That's no monkey business!

Fill in the circle next to the choice that best completes the sentence or answers the question.

1. What would make another good title for this passage?
   - (a) How to Train a Monkey ●
   - (b) Silly Monkeys
   - (c) Monkeys Who Lend a Hand
   - (d) People Helping Monkeys

2. In this passage, a **goal** is
   - (a) a habit.
   - (b) a plan.
   - (c) an action. ●
   - (d) a strength.

3. Another word for **active** is
   - (a) lively. ●
   - (b) lazy.
   - (c) loud.
   - (d) lovely.

4. The meaning of **pause** is
   - (a) start to play.
   - (b) press hard.
   - (c) pull up.
   - (d) stop for a short time. ●

5. In this passage, **patient** means
   - (a) a person getting medical treatment.
   - (b) nervous.
   - (c) understanding. ●
   - (d) a person who needs help.

6. Another word for **aim** is
   - (a) challenge.
   - (b) business.
   - (c) goal.
   - (d) need. ●

7. Based on the passage, you could say that capuchin monkeys are
   - (a) smart. ●
   - (b) difficult.
   - (c) strong.
   - (d) messy.

8. The meaning of **loyal** is
   - (a) faithful. ●
   - (b) little.
   - (c) skilled.
   - (d) famous.

Write Your Own

Think about how animals help people in different ways. On a separate sheet of paper, write to tell about another animal and how it helps people. Use at least three words from Units 1–3.

UNIT 4

Introducing the Words

Read the following folktale about a forest animal that learns a lesson. Notice how the highlighted words are used. These are the words you will be learning in this unit.

The Handsome Stag

(Folktale)

There was once a young stag that liked to use a shallow pool of water as a mirror. Every day, he would look down into it to notice how handsome he was. His antlers towered above his head. He moved them this way and that in order to get a better look.

One day, he carried on a silly conversation with himself.

"Ah, what beautiful antlers you have."

"They are nice. Look at your glorious back and neck, though. It's hard to say which part is the most beautiful."

"Don't be ridiculous. I insist that your antlers are the best part."

As the stag moved to get a better view of himself, he caught sight of his legs. Immediately, he felt gloomy. His legs were long and skinny. He wondered how they were able to hold up his large body and giant antlers. Then he sighed and went back to admiring his antlers until he became restless and bored. At last, he moved on to the field to eat grass.

Suddenly, the quiet of the afternoon was ended by the sounds of a hunter's horn and a loud bang. The dry branch of a tree was shattered by the gunshot. The stag raised his head in fear as the pieces of the branch fell to the ground. The stag was no coward. He knew, however, that even a hunter with little shooting talent could cause him harm. He began running. His long, slender legs carried him fast and far.

The stag spotted a passage inside a dark, thick part of the woods. He knew this path would take him to a stream. The hounds would lose his scent there. Then he could escape the hunting party. Faster and faster, he moved, his strong legs pushing him off the ground.

Then, just as the stag entered the thickest part of the forest, some low branches caught his antlers. He struggled and struggled. He pulled this way and that way. He had to avoid capture by the hunters.

The stag tried to free himself for a good five minutes. The branches poked his body, and his skin was scratched and sore. Finally, he pulled his antlers out and ran upstream.

When he was safe, the stag walked to a pool to drink some water and calm down. Before he put his head down to drink, he spotted the image of his body in the pool. All of a sudden, his antlers seemed heavy and useless.

Then he exclaimed, "Long have I admired my antlers and heavy body, but it was my slender, strong legs that saved me today."

Definitions

You were introduced to the words below in the passage on pages 36–37. Study the spelling, pronunciation, part of speech, and definition of each word. Write the word on the line in the sentence. Then read the synonyms and antonyms.

1. capture
(kap′ chər)

(n.) the act of catching or gaining control by force or skill

After the ___capture___ of the ship, the pirates divided its gold and silver.

(v.) to grab and hold onto; to hold the attention of

I will not read a book that does not ___capture___ my interest.

SYNONYMS: (v.) catch, seize, clutch, grasp
ANTONYMS: (v.) lose, release

2. coward
(kaŭ′ ərd)

(n.) one who has no courage or gets scared easily

I behaved like a ___coward___ during the thunderstorm.

SYNONYMS: weakling, wimp
ANTONYM: hero

3. exclaim
(eks klām′)

(v.) to speak with strong feelings or emotions; to cry out

When the phone rings, I always ___exclaim___, "I'll get it!"

SYNONYMS: yell, shout
ANTONYMS: whisper, murmur

4. gloomy
(glü′ mē)

(adj.) partly or completely dark; wearing a frown

The twins were both ___gloomy___ when they did not get their way.

SYNONYMS: unhappy, miserable
ANTONYMS: bright; happy, cheerful

5. insist
(in sist')

(v.) to state something or make a demand firmly

I continued to _____insist_____ that I did my homework even though I didn't have it with me.

SYNONYMS: declare, maintain, stress, require

6. passage
(pas' ij)

(n.) the act of moving from one place to another; a trip by sea or by air; a way in or out; a part of a written work or piece of music

The _____passage_____ from England to India took many days by boat.

SYNONYMS: tunnel, entrance, exit, opening; paragraph, section

7. restless
(rest' lis)

(adj.) unable to rest, relax, or be still; without rest or sleep

The baby was _____restless_____ all night.

SYNONYMS: nervous, uneasy, impatient
ANTONYMS: relaxed, peaceful, patient

8. shallow
(shal' ō)

(adj.) not deep; not showing much thought

The lake is _____shallow_____, so it is safe.

SYNONYMS: empty, simple
ANTONYM: deep

9. shatter
(shat' ər)

(v.) to break into many pieces; to cause much damage

Why did the mirror _____shatter_____?

SYNONYMS: smash, ruin

10. talent
(tal' ənt)

(n.) an ability to do something well; a skill or gift

You have a natural _____talent_____ for singing.

SYNONYM: knack

Match the Meaning

Choose the word whose meaning is suggested by the clue given.
Then write the word on the line provided.

1. Someone who _____ speaks in an excited way.
   a. captures   b. shatters   (c.) exclaims

2. A _____ sink is not very deep.
   (a.) gloomy   b. restless   c. shallow

3. To _____ an object is to grab and hold on to it.
   a. exclaim   b. insist   (c.) capture

4. A _____ is a person who is afraid or fearful.
   a. talent   b. passage   (c.) coward

5. A tunnel is a kind of _____.
   (a.) passage   b. capture   c. talent

6. If you have a skill, you have a _____.
   a. coward   (b.) talent   c. passage

7. When you can't sit still, you are _____.
   a. shallow   b. gloomy   (c.) restless

8. When a glass falls to the floor, it will probably _____.
   a. insist   b. capture   (c.) shatter

9. A clown can make both happy and _____ faces.
   a. restless   (b.) gloomy   c. shallow

10. When I _____ on something, I do not give up.
   a. capture   (b.) insist   c. exclaim

Because of all the rain, it was a **gloomy** day.

Synonyms

*Choose the word that is most nearly the **same** in meaning as the word or phrase in **dark print**. Then write your choice on the line provided.*

1. a **knack** for baking
   a. passage   b. coward   c. talent

   talent

2. a **paragraph** about birds
   a. capture   b. passage   c. coward

   passage

3. **maintain** their rights
   a. capture   b. shatter   c. insist on

   insist on

4. **break** into a hundred pieces
   a. capture   b. insist   c. shatter

   shatter

5. **uneasy** with worry
   a. gloomy   b. restless   c. shallow

   restless

Antonyms

*Choose the word that is most nearly **opposite** in meaning to the word or phrase in **dark print**. Then write your choice on the line provided.*

1. painted in **cheerful** colors
   a. gloomy   b. shallow   c. restless

   gloomy

2. **lose** the chess piece
   a. insist on   b. capture   c. shatter

   capture

3. **whisper** your answer
   a. capture   b. insist   c. exclaim

   exclaim

4. played a **hero** on stage
   a. talent   b. passage   c. coward

   coward

5. a **deep** swimming pool
   a. restless   b. gloomy   c. shallow

   shallow

Completing the Sentence

Choose the word from the box that best completes each item below. Then write the word on the line provided. (You may have to change the word's ending.)

capture	coward	exclaim
gloomy	insist	passage
restless	shallow	
shatter	talent	

Games

■ I like to play games with my brothers and sisters. We enjoy swimming in the neighborhood pool. We always stay in the _shallow_ end to make sure that we are safe.

■ We play baseball in our backyard. We know that if we hit the ball too hard, it might hit the house and _shatter_ a window. Then our dad would _exclaim_, "Hey, you broke the window!"

■ Jumping rope is fun. I _talent_ on being the first one to start jumping rope! That is because I get very _coward_ when I have to wait.

■ When I'm feeling _restless_, playing games can put me in a much better mood!

The Underground Railroad

■ In the years before the Civil War, many brave men and women risked their lives to free the slaves. It was very dangerous work and not a job for a _capture_.

■ One way that slaves escaped to freedom was by using a _passage_ known as the Underground Railroad.

■ Harriet Tubman showed a _insist_ for not getting caught by going back and forth on the Underground Railroad and helping many slaves escape.

■ It was wonderful how many slaves escaped and managed to avoid _gloomy_.

Word Associations

*Circle the letter next to the choice that best completes the sentence or answers the question. Pay special attention to the word in **dark print**.*

1. To **shatter** a vase is to
   a. break it into pieces.
   b. put flowers in it.
   c. wash it carefully.
   d. replace it.

2. Shallow water comes up to my
   a. shoulders.
   b. ears.
   c. ankles.
   d. neck.

3. If you read a **passage** from a story, you
   a. read the whole story.
   b. read a part of the story.
   c. read none of the story.
   d. understand the whole story.

4. It is best to **capture** a moth
   a. with a fan
   b. with a hook.
   c. with a net.
   d. with a pet.

5. Which shows that you **insist**?
   a. "May I come in?"
   b. "Will you join me?"
   c. "It has to be my way."
   d. "Whatever you think is okay."

6. A **coward** gets easily
   a. cold.
   b. scared.
   c. bored.
   d. thirsty.

7. Someone with **talent** might
   a. win a prize.
   b. go to sleep.
   c. go to the doctor.
   d. come in last.

8. Which words might you **exclaim**?
   a. "Where is the nearest store?"
   b. "My dog ran away!"
   c. "What kind of soup is that?"
   d. "What day is it?"

9. A person who is **gloomy** doesn't
   a. frown.
   b. swim.
   c. sigh.
   d. smile.

10. When I'm **restless**, I can't
   a. remember the words.
   b. keep still.
   c. stop yawning.
   d. get warm.

Word Study • Word Parts and Base Words

A **base word** is a complete word. You can add **word parts** to the beginning or end of a base word to make new words. The word *uncommon* is made of the base word *common* (page 8) and the beginning part *un-*. The word *gloomy* (page 38) is made up of the base word *gloom* and the ending part *-y*.

When you see a new word, look for a base word that you might know. This can help you figure out the meaning of the new word.

PRACTICE *Find the base word in each word. Write it on the line.*

1. strongest _____

2. misuse _____

3. helpful _____

4. freezing _____

5. rebuild _____

6. prettier _____

7. incorrectly _____

8. unhappiness _____

APPLY *Complete each sentence so that it makes sense. Pay attention to the word in dark print. Use what you know about the meaning of its base word.*

9. Because the weed was **firmly** rooted, _____

_____.

10. She will **rewrite** her science report because _____

_____.

11. I was **gasping** for air after _____

_____.

12. I chose the **mildest** soap because _____

_____.

13. Stay at the **shallower** end of the pool if _____

_____.

Work with a partner. Search through magazines or newspapers to find words that contain base words and other word parts. Make a list of the words you find. Underline the base words.

Shades of Meaning • Word Choice *capture, snatch, trap*

In the passage "The Handsome Stag" on pages 36–37, you read this sentence: *He had to avoid* **capture** *by the hunters*. Here, *capture* means "the act of catching and gaining control by force."

Capture has some synonyms, or words with almost the same meaning. But the words do not mean exactly the same thing as *capture*. Look at the chart below. Notice how the meanings of the synonyms are alike and different.

capture	When you **capture** something, you use force to catch it.
snatch	To **snatch** something is take or grab it in a hurry. It is often done in a rude or eager way.
trap	When you **trap** a person, you fool the person in order to catch him or her. When you trap an animal, you catch it in a cage or other box.

PRACTICE *Write the word from the chart that best completes each sentence.*

1. A thief may try to _____ a bike when the owner isn't looking.

2. I tried to _____ my brother into telling me about my gift.

3. I hope I can _____ the last piece of cake.

4. The pirates wanted to _____ the ship and sail it out of the port.

APPLY *Answer each question. Use the word (or one of the words) in dark print in your answer. Be sure to write complete sentences.*

5. How might you **trap** an insect?

_____

6. Why might a parent **snatch** something out of a child's hands?

_____

7. Would soldiers **trap** or **capture** an enemy fort? Why?

_____

8. Would a park ranger try to **snatch** or **trap** a wild bear? Why?

_____

Introducing the Words

Read the following journal article about a place to live and work while in space. Notice how the highlighted words are used. These are the words you will be learning in this unit.

The International Space Station

(Journal Article)

In a brilliant flash of light, the space shuttle blasts off from a launching pad. It is heading towards the International Space Station, or ISS. The shuttle carries food, equipment, and supplies to this place where astronauts live and work.

The ISS circles Earth more than 150 miles above our planet's atmosphere. If you looked down on the ISS, you would see something that looks like a giant bird. The bird's wings are actually solar panels. These capture energy for the station. The body of the bird contains labs and a place to eat, sleep, and relax.

The International Space Station circles Earth every 90 minutes.

Both Russia and the United States had plans for a space station. They knew that building a station together would be cheaper. Once the two countries were convinced that the project could be successful, they united their plans and worked together. Then other countries plunged into the project. These countries included Japan, Canada, France, and Italy.

Since the year 2000, humans have lived on the space station. Their days are very busy. Some astronauts complete experiments. Others work as mechanics, using robot arms to fix machines. Some workers grow plants.

All astronauts are highly trained. Their actions must be swift and sure when problems arise. Working in space is a dangerous job.

Sometimes, an astronaut must work outside. To do so, he or she puts on a space suit and takes a space walk outside the station. Conditions in space are harsh. It is very cold outside the space station, and there is no air there. A human cannot endure these conditions without the special suit.

Moving around in space is not easy either. Gravity doesn't hold the body in one place. There is always the danger of floating away! Astronauts must tie themselves down when sleeping, cooking, or exercising. On the plus side, heavy things seem light in space. Astronauts can lift and move huge pieces of equipment in space.

Astronaut taking a walk outside

The space station is as big as a football field. Keeping it clean is on the to-do list. Astronauts must cook for themselves, too. They must exercise two hours a day to stay strong. Free time is precious. It is often spent taking photographs, reading, writing e-mails home, or just glancing out the window at Earth below.

The International Space Station is a remarkable workplace in space. Exciting discoveries come from research being done there. Most important, countries are joining together to explore the ultimate frontier: space.

Definitions

You were introduced to the words below in the passage on pages 46–47. Study the spelling, pronunciation, part of speech, and definition of each word. Write the word on the line in the sentence. Then read the synonyms and antonyms.

1. **atmosphere**
   (at' mə sfir)

   (n.) the air that surrounds Earth; the feeling or mood in a room or place

   Earth's _atmosphere_ is made up of invisible gases.

   SYNONYM: environment

2. **brilliant**
   (bril' yənt)

   (adj.) sparkling or full of light; striking and shiny; very smart

   Many stars in the universe are _brilliant_ .

   SYNONYMS: bright, shining, vivid; clever
   ANTONYMS: dull, lifeless

3. **convince**
   (kən vins')

   (v.) to get someone to believe something or to do something; to win over

   It is easy to _convince_ *me to eat two pieces of carrot cake.*

   SYNONYMS: persuade, urge, coax
   ANTONYM: dissuade

4. **endure**
   (en dùr')

   (v.) to put up with; to continue in the same way for a long time

   I cannot _endure_ *your silly jokes!*

   SYNONYMS: suffer, bear; withstand, last

5. **glance**
   (glans)

   (v.) to look quickly; to bounce off a surface and fly off to one side

   I will _glance_ *at my watch from time to time to make sure my speech isn't too long.*

   (n.) a quick look

   One _glance_ *told me we would be close friends.*

   SYNONYMS: (v. & n.) glimpse, peek
   ANTONYM: (v. & n.) stare

6. harsh
(härsh)

(adj.) rough or unpleasant to the senses; unkind in voice or behavior

Try not to speak in a __harsh__ *tone, even when you are angry.*

SYNONYMS: crude; cruel, severe, demanding
ANTONYMS: smooth; pleasant, kind

7. plunge
(plunj)

(v.) to fall quickly; to quickly throw oneself down or into something

People looking for fun and thrills take the __plunge__ *in a roller coaster.*

(n.) the act of jumping in

Enjoy taking a __plunge__ *into the pool!*

SYNONYMS: (v.) dive, drop; (n.) dive, swim

8. precious
(pre′ shəs)

(adj.) very high-priced; loved and adored

Sapphires and rubies are __precious__ *jewels.*

SYNONYMS: valuable, special
ANTONYMS: worthless, valueless, ordinary

9. swift
(swift)

(adj.) able to move at a quick speed; quick to respond

The current was __swift__ *as the canoe reached the rapids.*

SYNONYMS: fast, rapid, speedy; ready
ANTONYMS: slow, gradual

10. unite
(yü nīt′)

(v.) to bring two or more parts together to make a whole

The team's players need to __unite__ *during a game.*

SYNONYMS: join, combine
ANTONYMS: break, split, undo, divide

Match the Meaning

Choose the word whose meaning is suggested by the clue given.
Then write the word on the line provided.

1. A very bright moon might be described as _brilliant_ .
   a. brilliant   b. harsh   c. swift

2. To _plunge_ something is to suffer through it.
   a. convince   b. plunge   c. endure

3. Sandpaper can feel _precious_ against
   your skin.
   a. harsh   b. brilliant   c. precious

4. A toy that is loved and adored is said to
   be _harsh_ .
   a. harsh   b. swift   c. precious

5. To _unite_ all the parts is to make
   a whole of them.
   a. convince   b. unite   c. endure

6. As soon as you walk into a room, you can feel its
   atmosphere .
   a. atmosphere   b. glance   c. plunge

7. A person who is able to respond quickly might be
   described as _swift_ .
   a. precious   b. harsh   c. swift

8. To _endure_ into a task is to jump into it and get it done.
   a. convince   b. endure   c. plunge

9. If you _glance_ at something, you give it a quick look.
   a. glance   b. convince   c. plunge

10. It is not always easy to _convince_ people to do
    something difficult.
    a. endure   b. plunge   c. convince

**Only a few brave people went
out in the harsh weather.**

Synonyms

Choose the word that is most nearly the **same** in meaning as the word or phrase in **dark print**. Then write your choice on the line provided.

1. **dive** into the sea
   a. unite   b. convince   c. plunge   *plunge*

2. a winter coat that will **last**
   a. endure   b. glance   c. unite   *endure*

3. **persuade** me to take dance lessons
   a. convince   b. endure   c. unite   *convince*

4. a smelly **environment**
   a. plunge   b. glance   c. atmosphere   *atmosphere*

5. gave the newspaper a **glimpse**
   a. glance   b. convince   c. unite   *glance*

6. a **valuable** gift
   a. harsh   b. precious   c. swift   *precious*

Antonyms

Choose the word that is most nearly **opposite** in meaning to the word or phrase in **dark print**. Then write your choice on the line provided.

1. **divide** the group
   a. endure   b. convince   c. unite   *unite*

2. a **lifeless** performance
   a. brilliant   b. swift   c. harsh   *brilliant*

3. a **gradual** movement
   a. brilliant   b. harsh   c. swift   *swift*

4. a **kind** comment
   a. harsh   b. precious   c. swift   *precious*

Completing the Sentence

Choose the word from the box that best completes each item below. Then write the word on the line provided. (You may have to change the word's ending.)

atmosphere	brilliant	convince
endure	glance	harsh
plunge	precious	
swift	unite	

Vacation

- My sister and I would love to take a _plunge_ into the cool ocean water.

- This year, we hope to _convince_ our parents to take the family to a theme park in Florida.

- We like the fun _endure_ in Florida. Everyone always seems to have such a good time!

- Also, after such a cold and _precious_ winter, we thought it would be nice to go someplace warm.

- My parents do not agree. They think it is too hot in Florida. It is hard for them to _atmosphere_ the heat.

- I know that wherever we go on vacation, we'll have many _unite_ memories!

VACATION

Math

- You can add and subtract using pencil and paper. You can also use mental math. Mental math is a _swift_ way to find sums and differences.

- In our class, there are some _brilliant_ math students. They can find sums and differences mentally with just a _glance_ at the numbers.

- In a math contest, the team members will _unite_ to solve challenging problems.

Word Associations

*Circle the letter next to the choice that best completes the sentence or answers the question. Pay special attention to the word in **dark print**.*

1. After a **brilliant** play, fans might
   a. yawn.
   b. boo.
   c. cheer.
   d. leave.

2. To **glance** at a magazine is to
   a. look at it slowly.
   b. look at it quickly.
   c. look at it carefully.
   d. throw it away.

3. Which animal is the most **swift**?
   a. deer
   b. snail
   c. turtle
   d. cow

4. Which is most likely to **endure**?
   a. paper
   b. brick
   c. fruit
   d. flowers

5. A **precious** gift is one that I will
   a. return for another.
   b. give to my dog.
   c. hope never to get.
   d. value forever.

6. Which are **harsh** words?
   a. "We love you."
   b. "You are clever."
   c. "I hate you."
   d. "This cheers me up."

7. Earth's **atmosphere** includes
   a. people and houses.
   b. animals and plants.
   c. oceans and mountains.
   d. air and gases.

8. You're most likely to **plunge**
   a. into the deep end of a pool.
   b. into a glass of juice.
   c. into a bucket of sand.
   d. into a cake mix.

9. Students would **unite** to sing
   a. off-key.
   b. softly.
   c. together.
   d. apart.

10. You need to **convince** me if you know that I
   a. already like your idea.
   b. do not agree with you.
   c. believe in you.
   d. will do whatever you say.

Word Study • Prefixes *re-*, *pre-*, *in-*

A **prefix** is a word part that is added to the beginning of a base word. A **base word** is a complete word. It makes sense as a word on its own. Adding a prefix can change the meaning of the word. It can also make a new word.

Prefix	Base Word		New Word		Meaning
re	+ unite	=	reunite	→	unite again
pre	+ heat	=	preheat	→	heat before
in	+ direct	=	indirect	→	not direct

Look at the prefixes and base words in the chart above. The prefix *re-* means "again." You can add *re-* to *unite* (page 49) to make the word *reunite*. *Reunite* means "unite again."

The prefix *pre-* means "before." The prefix *in-* sometimes means "not." Look at the chart for examples of words with the prefixes *pre-* and *in-*.

PRACTICE *Write the missing prefix. Then write the meaning of the new word.*

	Prefix		Base Word		New Word		Meaning
1.	pre	+	mix	=	premix	→	mix before
2.	re	+	fill	=	refill	→	fill again
3.	in	+	complete	=	incomplete	→	not complete
4.	re	+	read	=	reread	→	read again

APPLY *Complete each sentence with a word that contains the prefix* re-, pre-, *or* in-. *Choose from the words in the boxes above.*

5. Can you ___refill___ my glass of lemonade?

6. I wanted to get an A, but my homework was ___incomplete___.

7. My sister will ___premix___ the oven before baking the muffins.

8. When I didn't understand the story, my teacher said to ___read___ it.

 Write *Add the prefix* re-, pre-, *or* in- *to each word below to make a new word. Then write a sentence for each new word. You may use a dictionary if you need help.*

re**new**   in**correct**   re**dawn**

Shades of Meaning • Word Choice *glance, gaze, glare*

In the passage "The International Space Station" on pages 46–47, you read this sentence about free time on the space station: *It is often spent taking photographs, reading, writing e-mails home, or just **glancing** out the window at Earth below.* Here, *glancing* is a form of the verb *glance*. *Glance* means "to look quickly."·

Words may have similar meanings, but no two words have exactly the same meaning. Look at the words in the chart below. They all involve looking at someone or something. Read the words and their meanings. Notice how the words differ in meaning.

glance	When you **glance** at something, you look at it for just a moment.
gaze	When you **gaze**, you look at someone or something for a long time with amazement.
glare	When you **glare**, you look at someone or something in anger.

PRACTICE *Write the word from the chart that best replaces **look** in each sentence.*

1. I saw my sister **look** harshly at me after I ripped her bag. ___glare___

2. I always **look** around the park to see if any friends are there. ___glance___

3. Could you just take a quick **look** at my math homework? ___glance___

4. Mom would **look** into my eyes for hours when I was a baby. ___gaze___

5. I saw players on the losing team **look** at me when I scored my third goal.

   ___glance___

APPLY *Answer each question. Use the word in **dark print** in your answer. Be sure to write complete sentences.*

6. When might you **glance** at a clock?

   You might glance at a clock when checking time.

7. What might cause you to **gaze** at the sky?

   You might gaze at the sky when it's beautiful.

8. How can you tell whether someone is **glaring** at you?

   You can tell if someone is glaring at you if they are angry.

Introducing the Words

Read the following passage about a king who lived long ago. Notice how the highlighted words are used. These are the words you will be learning in this unit.

King Tut Then and Now

(Historical Nonfiction)

He was only nine years old when he became king. When his father died, he became the ruler, or pharaoh (fâr' ō). King Tut (short for Tutankhamun) ruled for only ten years. Yet he is one of Egypt's most famous kings.

King Tut isn't known for the wars he won. His fame isn't based on his wisdom or on the cities he built. Instead, he is known for the treasures he left behind.

King Tut ruled more than three thousand years ago. Little is known about his life. What we do know is based on what was found in his tomb.

When a pharaoh died, he was buried with things he might need on a journey. He would carry jewelry, perfume, and clothing. He would need a golden throne. A departing ruler would want to sail away in a ship. The tombs of pharaohs were filled with unbelievable riches.

Many Egyptian pharaohs were buried in the Valley of the Kings.

The Egyptian pharaohs were buried in the Valley of the Kings. In early Egyptian times, this area was guarded to prevent robberies. Still, robbers roamed the valley. They broke through the pharaohs' tombs and stole everything they could.

King Tut's tomb had been basically untouched. Grave robbers had broken in once, but they had not emptied the tomb. That is why the discovery in 1922 was so exciting. No one else had entered King Tut's tomb until an Englishman named Howard Carter discovered it. When he shone a light inside the closed space, he was speechless. He just stared at the superb treasures inside.

For months, Carter explored and studied the tomb. He found the pharaoh inside a solid gold casket. A gold mask covered his face. The room was brightly painted and bordered in gold.

Since then, many people have wondered how King Tut died. Some thought he was poisoned. Others thought he had fallen from a chariot during a race. He might have been killed while hunting lions or other fierce animals, as pharaohs were expected to do. These ideas made good stories, but the truth remained a mystery.

Modern science changed that. Scientists observed and tested King Tut's body. His body told a story about his short life.

Scientists are certain that Tutankhamun was not healthy. He probably couldn't ride a chariot. He definitely couldn't walk very far. King Tut had a bone disease that put him in constant pain. Pictures of the king show him clasping a cane. Many walking canes were found near him in his tomb.

To make matters worse, King Tut caught malaria more than once. Malaria is a disease that is carried by mosquitoes. In early Egyptian times, there was no cure for the disease. Most scientists think that malaria killed King Tut.

This gold mask is one of the treasures found in King Tut's tomb.

Definitions

You were introduced to the words below in the passage on pages 56–57. Study the spelling, pronunciation, part of speech, and definition of each word. Write the word on the line in the sentence. Then read the synonyms and antonyms.

1. border
(bôr′ dər)

(n.) the outer edge of an object; the line where two parts meet

We crossed the ___border___ into Canada.

(v.) to be next to or near something; to touch at the edge

One city can ___border___ a number of small towns.

SYNONYM: (n.) boundary

2. certain
(sûr′ tən)

(adj.) having no doubt; sure

I am ___certain___ I locked the door.

SYNONYMS: positive, confident, definite, fixed, settled, agreed
ANTONYMS: uncertain, unsure, indefinite

3. clasp
(klasp)

(n.) a device that holds parts together; a strong hold

I lost the ___clasp___ to my watch.

(v.) to hook something up; to hold tightly

My younger sister likes to ___clasp___ my hand.

SYNONYMS: (n.) buckle; grasp; (v.) fasten; grasp, seize
ANTONYMS: (v.) undo, loosen, unfasten

4. depart
(di pärt′)

(v.) to go away

I will ___depart___ for Miami soon.

SYNONYM: leave
ANTONYMS: stay, remain

5. fierce
(fērs)

(adj.) violent; wild or savage

The tiger that attacked the zookeeper was ___fierce___.

SYNONYMS: cruel, ferocious
ANTONYMS: mild, easygoing

6. journey
(jûr′ nē)

(n.) a long trip; a passage from one place to another

Where did you go on your ___Journey___ ?

(v.) to go on a trip; to travel

We plan to ___Journey___ *to Egypt.*

SYNONYMS: (n.) expedition, tour, voyage, outing;
(v.) tour, trek, go

7. observe
(əb zûrv′)

(v.) to see; to watch with close attention;
to stick to or obey

To understand how the bird gets its food,

the boy must ___observe___

its movements.

SYNONYMS: notice; abide

8. superb
(sü pûrb′)

(adj.) of the best quality

The acting and singing in the movie were ___Superb___ .

SYNONYMS: excellent, splendid, wonderful, marvelous, magnificent
ANTONYMS: inferior, ordinary

9. treasure
(tre′ zhər)

(n.) a collection of valuable objects; something worth a lot

The pirates guarded their ___treasure___ .

(v.) to care a great deal for

I ___treasure___ *my collection of foreign coins.*

SYNONYMS: (n.) wealth, riches; (v.) cherish, prize, appreciate
ANTONYMS: (v.) neglect, disregard

10. wisdom
(wiz′ dəm)

(n.) knowledge and good sense, especially as a result of experience

Grandparents have much ___wisdom___ *about life.*

SYNONYMS: judgment, understanding, intelligence
ANTONYM: ignorance

Match the Meaning

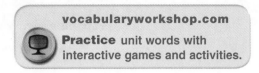
vocabularyworkshop.com
Practice unit words with
interactive games and activities.

Choose the word whose meaning is suggested by the clue given.
Then write the word on the line provided.

1. To cherish your friends is to ___treasure___ them.
   a. border b. clasp (c.) treasure

2. If you are sure about something, you are ___certain___.
   a. superb (b.) certain c. fierce

3. The edge of something is also called its
   ___border___.
   (a.) border b. journey c. wisdom

4. To ___depart___ from your route is
   to change it.
   a. clasp b. treasure (c.) depart

5. A knowing person is said to have
   ___wisdom___.
   a. journey (b.) wisdom c. treasure

6. Something excellent might be described as
   ___superb___.
   a. certain b. fierce (c.) superb

7. To ___journey___ is to go on a trip.
   (a.) journey b. clasp c. treasure

8. A latch is also called a ___clasp___.
   a. border b. wisdom (c.) clasp

9. A nurse will ___observe___ patients to see how
   they feel.
   (a.) observe b. treasure c. depart

10. Some wild animals are ___fierce___.
    a. certain b. superb (c.) fierce

The **journey** through the
desert was long and hot.

Synonyms

*Choose the word that is most nearly the **same** in meaning as the word or phrase in **dark print**. Then write your choice on the line provided.*

1. **notice** her face
   a. observe   b. border   c. journey   *observe*

2. **buckle** your seat belts
   a. depart   b. clasp   c. treasure   *clasp*

3. **travel** wherever you want
   a. border   b. journey   c. treasure   *journey*

4. gain more **knowledge**
   a. clasp   b. treasure   c. wisdom   *wisdom*

5. step over the **edge**
   a. journey   b. clasp   c. border   *border*

6. a **definite** opinion
   a. fierce   b. certain   c. superb   *certain*

Antonyms

*Choose the word that is most nearly **opposite** in meaning to the word or phrase in **dark print**. Then write your choice on the line provided.*

1. **disregard** his ideas
   a. treasure   b. border   c. clasp   *treasure*

2. an **ordinary** meal
   a. fierce   b. certain   c. superb   *Superb*

3. chose to **stay**
   a. border   b. treasure   c. depart   *depart*

4. an **easygoing** manner
   a. fierce   b. superb   c. certain   *fierce*

Completing the Sentence

Choose the word from the box that best completes each item below. Then write the word on the line provided. (You may have to change the word's ending.)

border	certain	clasp
depart	fierce	journey
observe	superb	
treasure	wisdom	

Traveling to a Foreign Country

■ When you plan to _____journey_____ to a foreign country, it is a good idea to learn how it is different from where you live.

■ Be sure to _____observe_____ all the rules of the country you are visiting. You might get into trouble if you don't obey them!

■ The rules may change again if you decide to cross the _____border_____ to visit another country.

■ Make _____certain_____ you know the train schedules.

■ That way, you will always know when trains arrive and _____depart_____.

Soccer

■ We have a _____superb_____ soccer team. Our coach thinks it's the best team she has ever had. We have very good players, and they score many goals each game.

■ Our coach has a lot of experience. She has much _____wisdom_____ to share with us. She knows that encouraging us to have fun and to get along with each other also helps us to win.

■ A player forgot to fasten the _____clasp_____ on the back of his shin guard, so it fell off during the game.

■ Soccer games can be very intense. The competition can be _____fierce_____! Still, we were always ready to take on the other teams. We finished this season on top.

■ Our team will always _____treasure_____ the trophy we won.

Word Study • Suffixes -ly, -ful, -less

A **suffix** is a word part that is added to the end of a **base word** to make a new word.

Look at the base words and suffixes in this chart. The suffix -ly usually means "in a certain way." You can add the suffix -ly to superb (page 59) to make the word superbly. Superbly means "in a superb or wonderful way."

Base Word	Suffix	New Word	Meaning
superb	+ **ly**	= superb**ly** →	in a superb or wonderful way
hope	+ **ful**	= hope**ful** →	full of hope
care	+ **less**	= care**less** →	without care

The suffix -ful means "full of." The suffix -less means "without." Look at the chart for examples of words with the suffixes -ful and -less.

PRACTICE *Write the missing suffix. Then write the meaning of the new word.*

Base Word	Suffix	New Word	Meaning
1. use	+ _less_	= useless →	_not useful_
2. quick	+ _ly_	= quickly →	_in a quick way_
3. harm	+ _ful_	= harmful →	_____
4. thought	+ _less_	= thoughtless →	_____

APPLY *Complete each sentence with a word that contains the suffix -ly, -ful or -less. Choose from the words in the boxes above.*

5. When it was my turn to play, I ran _____ onto the field.

6. My camera was _____ after I got sand in it.

7. Some snakebites can be _____ to people.

8. My sister skated _____ in the contest.

Write *The suffixes -ful and -less are opposites. Choose words with the suffix -ful or -less from the boxes above. Write the opposite of each word.*

Example: hope**ful**/hope**less**

Vocabulary for Comprehension

*Read the following passage in which some of the words you have studied in Units 4–6 appear in **dark print**. Then answer the questions on page 65.*

Nellie Bly: Star Reporter

Elizabeth Cochrane (1867–1922) always wanted to be a writer. She had big ideas and plenty of spirit. Elizabeth struggled before getting a chance at writing. Her break came when she sent a letter to a newspaper complaining about an article that it printed. The letter **captured** the attention of the paper's editor, who soon hired her. Elizabeth changed her name to Nellie Bly and started writing for the paper. In her job, she used her many **talents** to get important stories.

In 1887, Nellie moved to New York City, where she got a job working for a big newspaper. As Nellie grew more popular, her story ideas grew more daring. Once she pretended to be sick so she could **observe** the horrible conditions in a hospital. Another time, she **plunged** off a ferryboat into a river! She wanted to see how long it would take rescue workers to come to her aid.

In 1889, Nellie **convinced** her boss to send her on a trip around the world. She wanted to beat the record described in a book called *Around the World in Eighty Days.* From all over the world, Nellie sent back stories of her adventures and travels. When she completed the trip in just seventy-two days, she became world famous. Her **journey** was a huge success! Not only did Nellie beat the record, but she also proved that women could be brave and tough too.

In 1895, Nellie got married and left reporting. She returned more than twenty years later to report for the *New York Evening Journal.*

Fill in the circle next to the choice that best completes the sentence or answers the question.

1. This passage is mostly about
- (a) what Nellie did as a reporter.
- (b) when Nellie changed her name.
- (c) why Nellie was popular.
- (d) where Nellie traveled.

2. In this passage, **captured** means
- (a) lost.
- (b) caught.
- (c) missed.
- (d) discussed.

3. Another word for **talents** is
- (a) adventures.
- (b) hobbies.
- (c) articles.
- (d) skills.

4. In this passage, **observe** means
- (a) to pretend.
- (b) to change.
- (c) to watch.
- (d) to rescue.

5. You can tell from this passage that Nellie Bly is
- (a) tired.
- (b) afraid.
- (c) unhappy.
- (d) brave.

6. The meaning of **plunged** is
- (a) climbed.
- (b) jumped.
- (c) crawled.
- (d) walked.

7. Another word for **convinced** is
- (a) beat.
- (b) departed.
- (c) persuaded.
- (d) traveled.

8. The meaning of **journey** is
- (a) trip.
- (b) newspaper.
- (c) world.
- (d) train.

Write Your Own

During the seventy-two days that Nellie traveled around the world, she wrote about the many exciting adventures she experienced. Picture yourself on a similar journey around the world. On a separate sheet of paper, write a letter to your family back home that describes an adventure you have had during your travels. Use at least three words from Units 4–6.

REVIEW UNITS 1–6

Classifying

Choose the word from the box that goes best with each group of words. Write the word on the line provided. Then explain what the words have in common. The first one has been done for you.

bitter   certain   exclaim

gloomy   patient   pause

~~restless~~   superb

swift   wander

1. thoughtless, careless, worthless, _____ restless _____

   The words have the same suffix.

2. _____, walk, skip, run

   _____

3. happy, cheerful, sad, _____

   _____

4. quick, rapid, speedy, _____

   _____

5. unsure, doubtful, possible, _____

   _____

6. clause, laws, thaws, _____

   _____

7. doctor, nurse, aide, _____

   _____

8. _____, whisper, declare, shout

   _____

9. poor, decent, fine, _____

   _____

10. _____, sour, salty, sweet

   _____

Completing the Idea

Complete each sentence so that it makes sense. Pay attention to the word in **dark print**.

1. When it rains, my parents **insist** that I _____.

2. With a quick **glance** over my shoulder, I _____.

3. When a stream is **shallow**, _____.

4. Students in our school **unite** to _____.

5. Water is a precious **resource** because _____.

6. When I came to the narrow **passage**, I _____.

7. When the weather is **mild**, I _____.

8. The **active** baby _____.

9. When I can't **endure** the summer heat, I _____.

10. Whenever I set a **goal** for myself, I _____.

11. When the **fierce** wind blew, _____.

12. I spoke in a **harsh** tone when I _____.

13. On rainy days, I **prefer** to _____.

14. You can **ruin** a painting if _____.

15. To **trace** the picture, I _____.

Writing Challenge

Write two sentences using the word **faint**. In the first sentence, use **faint** as a verb. In the second sentence, use **faint** as an adjective.

1. _____

2. _____

REVIEW UNITS 1–6

Introducing the Words

Read the following report about a bell that is part of American history. Notice how the highlighted words are used. These are the words you will be learning in this unit.

The Liberty Bell

(Report)

The Liberty Bell is far from perfect. It never rings, and it has a huge crack. Yet it is a well-known symbol of the United States. To people from coast to coast, it means freedom. Why?

The Liberty Bell has a rich history. It was made in England and sent to Philadelphia in 1752. The bell cracked when it was first tested. Some people accused the makers of doing a poor job when making it. Rather than return it, the city of Philadelphia decided to fix it. The city's leaders hired two clever metalworkers. The men melted the bell down and made another bell, imitating the original. Then the new bell was hung in a tower. It was used to call lawmakers together.

On July 4, 1776, the Declaration of Independence was completed. Many people believe that the bell was rung at this time. However, experts who have explored its history say that the event never happened. In fact, some think that the steeple where the bell was hung was in a delicate condition. It was not strong enough to hold a ringing bell.

Here is one story about the ringing of the bell on that day. In the 1840s, a writer named George Lippard wrote a tale about a bell ringer who wanted to ring the bell when the Declaration of Independence was completed. When the time came, he rang the bell in triumph. The sound was heard all over Philadelphia. Many Americans read and loved the story. From then on, the Liberty Bell was a symbol of independence.

Liberty Bell

The Liberty Bell on one of its journeys

In 1846, the Liberty Bell was rung to honor the birthday of George Washington. He was the country's first president and another symbol of independence. The bell's clear sound pierced the air, but the ringing also had another effect. It widened a crack that had been forming. By noon, the ringing sounded terrible. Since that time, the bell has been silent.

Just because the Liberty Bell no longer rang, it did not lose its importance as a symbol of freedom. Beginning in the late 1800s, the Liberty Bell was displayed across the country and was seen by many people. The Liberty Bell reminded Americans of their past and of how they had worked together for freedom.

Today, the Liberty Bell hangs in a glass building in Philadelphia. In the past, hearing its ring was a rare event, and now it does not ring at all. Still, it sings a song of freedom for all Americans.

Liberty Bell Center in Philadelphia

Definitions

You were introduced to the words below in the passage on pages 68–69. Study the spelling, pronunciation, part of speech, and definition of each word. Write the word on the line in the sentence. Then read the synonyms and antonyms.

1. accuse
(ə kyüz')

(v.) to say that someone or something has done wrong; blame

Please don't ___accuse___ me of being lazy!

SYNONYM: tattle
ANTONYMS: praise, absolve

2. clever
(kle' vər)

(adj.) having or showing a quick mind; bright, smart

The ___clever___ student answered every question correctly.

SYNONYMS: skillful, cunning, sharp, intelligent
ANTONYMS: dull, dumb, unintelligent, stupid, slow

3. coast
(kōst)

(n.) the land near the sea or ocean

California is on the Pacific ___coast___ of the United States.

(v.) to move along without any power or effort; to slide down a slope

Our sleds will ___coast___ down the hill.

SYNONYMS: (n.) seashore, seaside, waterfront, beach; (v.) glide, ride

4. delicate
(del' i kət)

(adj.) easily broken or damaged; requiring care or skill

Do not touch that ___delicate___ teacup, please!

SYNONYMS: dainty, fragile, weak, frail
ANTONYMS: sturdy, hard, coarse, rough

5. explore
(ik splôr')

(v.) to travel; to discover; to look into or study something

I would like to ___explore___ the new neighborhood.

SYNONYMS: examine, investigate, analyze, search, research

6. imitate
(i′ mə tāt)

(v.) to copy someone's movements or expressions; to appear like something else

I love to ___imitate___ the actor's funny face.

SYNONYMS: mimic, resemble, repeat, reproduce

7. pierce
(pērs)

(v.) to make a hole or opening; to run into or through something, as with a pointed tool or weapon

Use scissors to ___pierce___ the plastic wrap.

SYNONYMS: stab, perforate, enter, penetrate

8. rare
(râr)

(adj.) not often found, seen, or happening; unusually valuable or good; not fully cooked

It is ___rare___ for a pitcher to hit many home runs.

SYNONYMS: infrequent; unusual, uncommon
ANTONYMS: frequent; ordinary, usual, common, normal

9. symbol
(sim′ bəl)

(n.) something that stands for something else; a written sign that is used to represent an operation or a calculation

The Statue of Liberty is a ___symbol___ of freedom.

SYNONYMS: mark, note, token, emblem

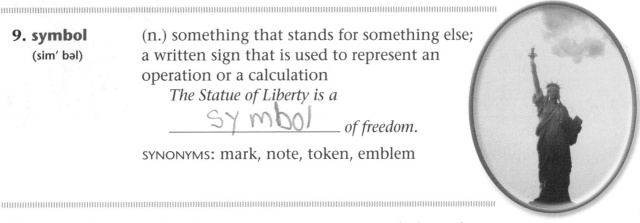

10. triumph
(trī′ əmf)

(n.) an important success or win; a feeling of happiness that comes from winning

Winning the battle was a ___triumph___ for them.

(v.) to succeed

The basketball team will ___triumph___ in the end.

SYNONYMS: (n.) victory, achievement; (v.) overcome, conquer
ANTONYMS: (n.) loss, defeat; (v.) lose

Match the Meaning

Choose the word whose meaning is suggested by the clue given.
Then write the word on the line provided.

1. A strip of land along the water is called a _coast_.
   a. triumph   b. symbol   c. coast

2. Smart people may also be described as _clever_.
   a. rare   b. clever   c. delicate

3. To _explore_ is to go to a new or unknown place.
   a. imitate   b. explore   c. accuse

4. When you _accuse_ people, you are saying they are doing something wrong.
   a. explore   b. pierce   c. accuse

5. Very unusual objects are said to be _rare_.
   a. rare   b. clever   c. delicate

6. To _imitate_ people is to copy them.
   a. triumph   b. imitate   c. coast

7. A _triumph_ might also be called a victory.
   a. triumph   b. symbol   c. coast

8. A pin might _pierce_ a balloon.
   a. triumph   b. pierce   c. accuse

9. Something that is easily broken is _delicate_.
   a. clever   b. rare   c. delicate

10. The mathematical _symbol_ for addition is the plus sign.
    a. coast   b. triumph   c. symbol

The hikers were excited to **explore** a cave they had never been in before.

Synonyms

Choose the word that is most nearly the **same** in meaning as the word or phrase in **dark print**. Then write your choice on the line provided.

1. the beauty of the **seashore**
a. symbol   b. triumph   c. coast

coast

2. **investigate** the caves
a. imitate   b. explore   c. pierce

explore

3. **mimic** my voice
a. pierce   b. imitate   c. accuse

imitate

4. **stab** the meat
a. explore   b. coast   c. pierce

pierce

5. **blame** the dog
a. accuse   b. pierce   c. triumph

accuse

6. a **sign** of freedom
a. symbol   b. coast   c. triumph

symbol

Antonyms

Choose the word that is most nearly **opposite** in meaning to the word or phrase in **dark print**. Then write your choice on the line provided.

1. a **dumb** thing to do
a. delicate   b. clever   c. rare

clever

2. **sturdy** glass plates
a. clever   b. delicate   c. rare

delicate

3. a surprising **defeat**
a. triumph   b. coast   c. symbol

triumph

4. a **common** complaint
a. clever   b. delicate   c. rare

rare

Completing the Sentence

Choose the word from the box that best completes each item below. Then write the word on the line provided. (You may have to change the word's ending.)

accuse	clever	coast
delicate	explore	imitate
pierce	rare	
symbol	triumph	

Holidays

■ Holidays give people a chance to be creative and to think of _____clever_____ costumes.

■ On Halloween this year, I'm going to dress up as my favorite singer. I will _____imitate_____ her.

■ When children visit, we put our glasses on high shelves. Glasses are _____delicate_____ and break easily.

■ May Day is an important holiday in England. It is _____symbol_____, however, for Americans to celebrate that holiday.

■ It is always good to _____explore_____ new ways of making the holidays fun.

Politics

■ Candidates have to work very hard to get votes. If they _____coast_____ along instead of working hard, they will probably not win the election.

■ Unfortunately, it is common for candidates in a race to _____accuse_____ each other of not telling the truth.

■ Some politicians speak so loudly that their voices almost _____pierce_____ the air.

■ The _____symbol_____ for the Republican Party is the elephant. The sign of the Democratic Party is the donkey.

■ Usually, the candidate who loses the race congratulates the winner on his or her _____imitate_____.

Word Associations

Circle the letter next to the choice that best completes the sentence or answers the question. Pay special attention to the word in dark print.

1. If you **accuse** me, you might say,
   a. "It's all your fault."
   b. "Thanks for your help."
   c. "I'll take the blame."
   d. "You are in the clear."

2. It's **rare** to find a
   a. four-wheeled car.
   b. four-legged cat.
   c. four-room apartment.
   d. four-leaf clover.

3. Which tool is used to **pierce**?
   a. a paintbrush
   b. a wrench
   c. a drill
   d. a ruler

4. A **delicate** object would be very easy to
   a. break.
   b. build.
   c. carry.
   d. copy.

5. To **imitate** a kangaroo, you might
   a. read and write.
   b. dance and sing.
   c. hop and wear a pouch.
   d. chirp and spread your arms like wings.

6. A race car could be a **symbol** of
   a. music.
   b. speed.
   c. food.
   d. hate.

7. If you live along the **coast** of Texas, you are probably
   a. a long way from the water.
   b. far from home.
   c. on a mountain top.
   d. near the water.

8. I **explore** if I go to a place I
   a. visit every day.
   b. know inside and out.
   c. have never been to before.
   d. think is no fun.

9. If you **triumph**, you are the
   a. loser.
   b. quitter.
   c. fighter.
   d. winner.

10. It takes a **clever** dog to
   a. bark at strangers.
   b. learn to "shake hands."
   c. chase cats and squirrels.
   d. chew on bones.

Word Study • Homophones

Homophones are words that sound alike but have different spellings and meanings. For example, *symbol* (page 71) and *cymbal* are homophones. A *symbol* is something that stands for something else. A *cymbal* is a round, metal instrument that makes a crashing sound.

Read this sentence: *We used a picture of a **cymbal** as a **symbol** of our drum group*. Notice how the sentence illustrates the meaning of each homophone.

Look at the chart to find the spellings and meanings of other homophones.

brake	a stopping device
break	to split into pieces; to damage or make no longer usable
sew	to stitch together or mend using a needle and thread
sow	to plant or scatter seeds in the ground
heal	to make well
heel	the back part of the foot below the ankle

PRACTICE *Underline the homophone that completes each sentence.*

1. My mother had to (**sew, sow**) my costume for the school play.

2. The driver had to use the emergency (**brake, break**) to stop the car.

3. My broken elbow will take three months to (**heal, heel**).

4. The farmer will (**sew, sow**) corn in his field.

5. Please be careful not to (**brake, break**) my new computer game!

6. I developed a sore (**heal, heel**) from my tight sneakers.

APPLY *Use each homophone pair in a sentence. Write the sentence on the line provided. Be sure to use the correct meaning of each word.*

7. **sew, sow** _____

8. **brake, break** _____

9. **heal, heel** _____

 Make up a riddle for one of the words in the homophone pairs below. Ask a partner to guess the word and spell it.

        ate/eight   **berry/bury**

        Example: I am a juicy, little fruit. What am I? (a berry)

Shades of Meaning • Idioms 1

In the passage "The Liberty Bell" on pages 68–69, you read this sentence: *To people from coast to coast, it means freedom.* Here, the word *coast* means "land near the sea or ocean."

An **idiom** is an expression that has a special meaning. You cannot figure out its meaning from the individual words. Here is an example: *Before we brought in Mom's surprise, we checked and made sure that the coast was clear.* Here, the idiom *coast was clear* has nothing to do with land near the ocean. Instead, it means "there was no one around."

PRACTICE *Read each sentence. Figure out the meaning of each idiom in dark print. Write the number of the sentence next to the meaning of the idiom.*

1. I thought writing the report would be difficult, but it was a **piece of cake**.

2. To win a race, you must be ready to start running **at the drop of a hat**.

3. "If you can't say something nice, **bite your tongue**!"

4. I was **under the weather** for a few days, but now I am well.

_____ don't speak

_____ easy

_____ right away, instantly

_____ sick

APPLY *Read each sentence. Figure out the meaning of the idiom in dark print. Write the meaning on the line provided.*

5. Mom loves Mittens more than she loves our other cats. She says, "He's the

   apple of my eye!" _____

6. A wave destroyed my sand castle, but I **went back to square one** and built

   another one. _____

7. My piano teacher **bends over backwards** to make sure I understand each

   lesson. _____

8. Dad gets up **at the crack of dawn** each day to watch the morning news on

   television. _____

Introducing the Words

Read the following journal article about an army from the past. Notice how the highlighted words are used. These are the words you will be learning in this unit.

The Terracotta Army

(Journal Article)

In 1974, workmen who were digging a well in northwestern China discovered an ancient secret. They uncovered the first of many life-size clay soldiers in a tomb. These soldiers were made of a kind of clay called terracotta. Over time, workers at the tomb exposed more than 8,000 warriors and horses.

The terracotta warriors and horses have been standing in the tomb for more than 2,000 years. Who were these statues supposed to be? What were they doing in the ground? Scientists have been unlocking the mystery for more than thirty years now.

About 2,200 years ago, an emperor named Qin Shi Huang Di (CHĒN SHĒ HWÄŊ dē) ruled the land now called China. To gain control, he fought wars all over the land, even in the remote areas.

When Qin lived, it was the custom to bury a ruler with things he might need after he died. Qin had many enemies, so he felt he needed an army to protect his tomb. That's why the warriors look as if they are prepared to fight.

The terracotta warriors are extremely lifelike. You can see strands of hair that cling to the neck. Every statue has a different face, hairstyle, and expression.

Emperor
Qin Shi Huang Di

Qin was not timid about making the tomb grand. Scientists believe it took 36 years to build. At least 700,000 people worked to complete it. Also, Qin wanted to take with him everything he had when he was alive. He made sure his body would be surrounded by silks, pearls, and gems.

Qin also had statues of acrobats, singers, musicians, and dancers to entertain him. All these people would have performed for the emperor.

There were also statues of pigs, dogs, horses, and sheep in the tomb. At one time, the horses had leather straps with shiny bronze metal. The bronze still shines, but the leather decayed long ago.

The statues were painted in reds, blues, greens, and purples. When scientists took one statue out into the dry climate, the paint disappeared. Horrified, they looked for ways to save the colors in the other statues.

The emperor Qin accomplished a lot during his rule. He began using money for trading. He improved the systems for writing and for using weights and measures. The name *China* probably came from the word *Qin*.

Scientists have learned a lot about how emperors lived by exploring Qin's tomb. Unfortunately, vandals, people who set out to destroy things on purpose, had disturbed part of Qin's tomb. Some things were also damaged by water or fire. Scientists have worked to piece together what was once there.

Today, scientists are still uncovering more treasures from the tomb. With each discovery, we find out more and more about life in China so long ago.

A soldier in the terracotta army

Definitions

You were introduced to the words below in the passage on pages 78–79. Study the spelling, pronunciation, part of speech, and definition of each word. Write the word on the line in the sentence. Then read the synonyms and antonyms.

1. ancient
(ān′ shənt)

(adj.) very old; early in history

The fossil remains are ___ancient___ .

SYNONYMS: antique, old-fashioned
ANTONYMS: new, recent

2. climate
(klī′ mət)

(n.) the usual weather conditions of a place

I don't like that moist, hot ___climate___ .

SYNONYMS: atmosphere, environment, temperature

3. cling
(kliŋ)

(v.) to hold on firmly; to have a strong attachment to or feeling for something or someone

As a child, I used to ___cling___ *to my mother.*

SYNONYMS: stick, attach, grasp
ANTONYM: release

4. custom
(kus′ təm)

(n.) a common practice; the way people do things year after year

Eating turkey and stuffing is a ___custom___ *celebrated by many people on Thanksgiving.*

SYNONYMS: tradition, habit

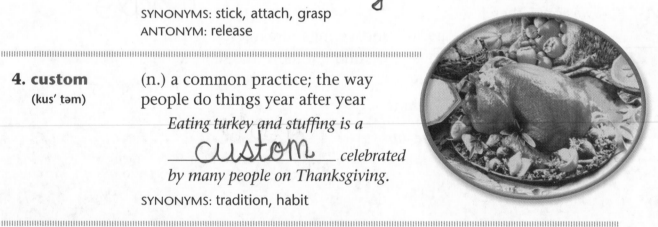

5. decay
(di kā′)

(v.) to slowly decline or fall into ruin

The salt water caused the dock to ___decay___ .

(n.) the slow decline of something; a wearing away

Go to the dentist twice a year to try to avoid tooth ___decay___ .

SYNONYMS: (v.) rot, spoil, decompose, disintegrate; (n.) weakening
ANTONYMS: (v.) flourish, bloom, thrive

6. disturb
(di stûrb')

(v.) to make upset or uneasy

We tried not to __disturb__ *their sleep.*

SYNONYMS: interrupt, stop, disrupt, alarm
ANTONYMS: calm, soothe

7. expose
(ik spōz')

(v.) to uncover or open to view; to make something known

I promise not to __expose__ *their secrets.*

SYNONYMS: show, reveal, disclose, display
ANTONYMS: cover, hide, disguise, mask

8. perform
(pər fôrm')

(v.) to carry out a task; to act or entertain

The couple was asked to __perform__ *the play on Wednesday.*

SYNONYMS: sing, dance; achieve, fulfill, do, function

9. remote
(ri mōt')

(adj.) far removed in distance or time, out of the way; unlikely; very slight

We drove to a __remote__ *cabin in the woods.*

SYNONYMS: faraway, distant, secluded
ANTONYMS: near, nearby, open

10. timid
(ti' məd)

(adj.) lacking courage or confidence

I was too __timid__ *to talk to the new teacher.*

SYNONYMS: cautious, shy, meek
ANTONYMS: bold, brash, daring, determined, confident

Match the Meaning

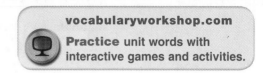

Choose the word whose meaning is suggested by the clue given.
Then write the word on the line provided.

1. To interrupt a class is to ___disturb___ it.
   a. cling   b. decay   c. disturb

2. A(n) ___remote___ place is far away.
   a. ancient   b. timid   c. remote

3. Something very old is considered
   ___ancient___.
   a. timid   b. ancient   c. remote

4. The ___custom___ of a region refers to its
   weather patterns.
   a. custom   b. climate   c. decay

5. To ___cling___ is to hold on tightly.
   a. cling   b. perform   c. expose

6. If you ___expose___ something, you
   uncover it.
   a. decay   b. perform   c. expose

7. A(n) ___timid___ person lacks confidence
   and courage.
   a. timid   b. remote   c. ancient

8. To put on a show is to ___Perform___.
   a. cling   b. perform   c. disturb

9. A ___decay___ is an event that is repeated
   regularly.
   a. climate   b. decay   c. custom

10. The decline of something means its ___climate___.
    a. climate   b. custom   c. decay

The tropical **climate** in the Caribbean Islands makes them a popular vacation spot.

Synonyms

Choose the word that is most nearly the **same** in meaning as the word or phrase in **dark print**. Then write your choice on the line provided.

1. **fulfill** your duties
   a. cling   b. perform   c. decay

   perform

2. meat that has **spoiled**
   a. clung   b. decayed   c. disturbed

   decayed

3. **hold** on to the wall
   a. cling   b. decay   c. expose

   cling

4. the city's **weather**
   a. decay   b. custom   c. climate

   climate

5. a family's **tradition**
   a. custom   b. climate   c. decay

   custom

6. news that **upsets**
   a. clings   b. performs   c. disturbs

   disturbs

Antonyms

Choose the word that is most nearly **opposite** in meaning to the word or phrase in **dark print**. Then write your choice on the line provided.

1. **new** coins
   a. ancient   b. remote   c. timid

   ancient

2. a **nearby** road
   a. timid   b. ancient   c. remote

   remote

3. a **bold** reaction
   a. remote   b. ancient   c. timid

   timid

4. **cover** the wound
   a. cling   b. expose   c. perform

   expose

Completing the Sentence

Choose the word from the box that best completes each item below. Then write the word on the line provided. (You may have to change the word's ending.)

ancient	climate	cling
custom	decay	disturb
expose	perform	
remote	timid	

Gorillas and Their Environment

■ Many gorillas live in jungles and tropical rain forests.

■ The ___climate___ of a tropical rain forest is very wet, with very high temperatures.

■ A young gorilla will _____ to its mother's back when traveling in the jungle.

■ Female gorillas may seem more _____ than males, but in fact they are just as brave.

■ Gorillas sleep for a few hours after they eat. It is wise not to ___disturb___ them while they sleep!

Our Theater

■ Welcome to our theater! I know it looks old and in a state of _____, but I promise you that it will stand up just fine!

■ This theater was once a beautiful place. Just push back the curtains to _____ the lovely murals on the wall.

■ This evening, we will _____ a show for you.

■ Every year, it is our _____ to put on a show celebrating different countries.

■ This play is based on an ___ancient___ Egyptian myth. It is a very old story of how the planet Earth was born.

■ I know the chances that I'll become a great star are _____. If that does happen, however, I will be happy to share my secrets of success!

Word Associations

*Circle the letter next to the choice that best completes the sentence or answers the question. Pay special attention to the word in **dark print**.*

1. Which is **ancient**?
   a. a computer
   b. a bicycle
   c. a puppy
   d. a mummy

2. A **custom** is something you
   a. do on a regular basis.
   b. don't like to do.
   c. are forced to do.
   d. don't do at all.

3. To **expose** house plants to light, you might put them
   a. near a window.
   b. in a closet.
   c. under the bed.
   d. in the basement.

4. A **timid** person might try to
   a. show off.
   b. make a speech.
   c. be a hero.
   d. shy away from a group.

5. When an apple starts to **decay**, it
   a. tastes sweet and juicy.
   b. goes brown and mushy.
   c. is fresh and crispy.
   d. needs to be washed.

6. People who study the **climate** of a place pay attention to
   a. its people.
   b. its weather.
   c. its traffic.
   d. its cities.

7. If I **disturb** you, I should say,
   a. "Have you read a good book?"
   b. "Will you come to my party?"
   c. "Excuse me for bothering you."
   d. "Please take a bath."

8. To **perform** a task, you must
   a. finish it.
   b. stay away from it.
   c. quit before the end.
   d. ask an adult for help.

9. A **remote** cabin would have
   a. many rooms.
   b. many visitors.
   c. few neighbors.
   d. many houses nearby.

10. If you **cling** to an idea, you
    a. hold on to it.
    b. forget it.
    c. ignore it.
    d. change your mind.

Word Study • Context Clues 2

The **context clues** in a sentence can help you figure out the meaning of a word you do not know. There are many types of context clues. You have learned how to look for a definition. You can also look for examples that can help you figure out the meaning of a word.

Example

*The stove, dishwasher, and microwave are different kitchen **appliances**.*

The examples are stove, dishwasher, and microwave. These things help you understand that appliances are machines that perform specific jobs.

PRACTICE *Read each sentence. Use context clues to figure out the meaning of the word in **dark print**. Write the number of each sentence next to the correct meaning.*

1. He showed us **vessels** such as sailboats, canoes, and kayaks.

2. We felt **sorrowful** and upset when we left our new friends.

3. Apple, peach, and cherry **blossoms** all come from blooming fruit trees.

4. The beach was covered with **litter** such as cans, bottles, and wrappers.

_____ trash

_____ boats

_____ unhappy

_____ flowers

APPLY *Read each sentence. Underline the words that help you figure out the meaning of the word in **dark print**. Then write a definition and a new sentence for the word.*

5. My **chores** at home are setting the table and walking the dog.

Definition: _____

New Sentence: _____

6. The spaceship was an **extraordinary**, or uncommon, sight in the sky.

Definition: _____

New Sentence: _____

Speak *Give examples of things that belong in the same group. Ask your partner to name the group.*

Example: Partner 1: *hammer, screwdriver, wrench*

Partner 2: tools

Shades of Meaning • Words That Describe People 1

In the passage "The Terracotta Army" on pages 78–79, you read this sentence: *Qin was not **timid** about making the tomb grand.* The sentence tells us that Qin was bold. He was not afraid to say what he wanted the tomb to look like.

All the words in the chart describe people. Learning the words will help you choose the right word to use when you describe people in speaking and writing.

timid	People who are **timid** are shy. They may lack courage or confidence.
friendly	People who are **friendly** are kind and pleasant.
helpful	People who are **helpful** are ready to assist others.

PRACTICE *Write the word from the chart that best describes the person speaking.*

1. I see that you are new here. What's your name? _____

2. Let me take out the recycling bin for you. _____

3. Can I let someone else read my report to the class? _____

4. Would you like me to put away the dishes? _____

5. I don't want to walk into the party by myself. _____

6. Hi there! Do you want to eat lunch with us today? _____

APPLY *Think about a person you know who fits each description. Describe the person. Explain how he or she fits the description.*

7. **friendly** _____

_____

8. **helpful** _____

_____

9. **timid** _____

_____

Introducing the Words

Read the following passage about a talented sister and brother. Notice how the highlighted words are used. These are the words you will be learning in this unit.

The Talent Show

(Realistic Fiction)

"**I** can't sing in the talent show without you," Sundara said.

"I can't sing even *with* you," her brother Vijay replied. "I am so bashful. I would probably melt right on the stage."

"That's a silly remark," Sundara said. "You sing really well."

"I'm shy! Give me a break!"

Sundara did not give in. "Please, please, please!" she begged. "You know this talent show benefits the food bank."

"Okay, I'll consider it," Vijay said. "Don't get your hopes up, though!"

Sundara kept trying. "But we could win. You have a terrific voice," she said.

Vijay said, "You know I don't like to compete with other people."

"That's fine," Sundara said. "Just rehearse with me then."

For the next hour, Sundara and Vijay practiced together while their father played the piano. Finally, Vijay agreed to sing with his sister.

The morning of the talent show, Vijay was very nervous. Then at breakfast, everything changed.

"Good morning," Sundara said in a low moan.

"What's wrong?" Vijay asked.

Then Sundara sneezed.

"Get away!" Vijay said. He shielded his face almost as a reflex.

Sundara couldn't speak. She wrote a short note on a pad of paper and showed it to him.

My throat's sore.
I can't talk.

Vijay was suddenly happy. "Too bad," he said. "No duet tonight!"
Sundara started scribbling and then thrust another note at him.

*Don't think for a **brief** moment
that you aren't singing!*

Vijay started to protest. Sundara grabbed the pad again. She wrote:

*Stop it! You have the **ability**.
Now just do it—for the
food bank!*

Vijay suddenly felt selfish. Of course, he had to sing. It was the right
thing to do.

That day, he kept busy to avoid thinking about the show. He practiced
the song with his dad first. Then he rode his bike, washed the car, and
did some homework. A few hours later, he was onstage. It was his
turn to sing.

Before Vijay knew it, the song had ended. As he walked
backstage, his mom hugged him and said, "Your song was
delightful!"

Ms. Spencer, the show's host, now took the stage. She
had two announcements. First, the students had raised over
$1,000 for the food bank. Second, the judges had made
their decision. Ms. Spencer announced the third-place and
second-place winners. Vijay was relieved that his name
wasn't called.

Next, Ms. Spencer said, "It's time to announce the first-
place winner." She paused and said, "Let's have Vijay
Rana come to the stage!" Ms. Spencer handed him a
trophy and then asked him to say a word or two.

Vijay said, "Thank you so much. This is a
great honor. I want to dedicate this trophy
to my sister. After all, I wouldn't be here if it
weren't for her!"

Definitions

You were introduced to the words below in the passage on pages 88–89. Study the spelling, pronunciation, part of speech, and definition of each word. Write the word on the line in the sentence. Then read the synonyms and antonyms.

1. ability
(ə bil′ ə tē)

(n.) the power or skill to do something

Lifeguards must have the ___ability___ to swim well.

SYNONYMS: talent, capacity, capability
ANTONYMS: inability, powerlessness

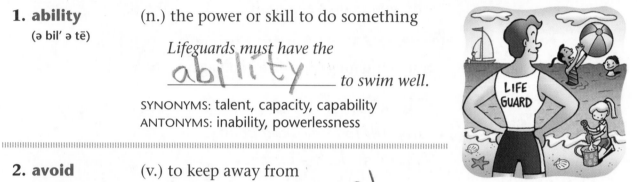

2. avoid
(ə void′)

(v.) to keep away from

They tried to ___avoid___ the mud, but they were not successful.

SYNONYMS: evade, escape, elude
ANTONYM: seek

3. bashful
(bash′ fəl)

(adj.) shy, not at ease, especially in a social setting

Why were you so ___bashful___ at the party?

SYNONYMS: timid, reserved, awkward, uneasy
ANTONYMS: bold, brash, aggressive, outgoing

4. brief
(brēf)

(adj.) short in time, amount, or length

A three-day vacation is too ___brief___ for me.

SYNONYMS: quick, fleeting, concise
ANTONYMS: long, lengthy, extended

5. compete
(kəm pēt′)

(v.) to try for something, such as a prize; to take part in a game or contest; to play against another or others

In gym, students might ___compete___ in the 50-yard dash.

SYNONYMS: strive, rival, contend, challenge

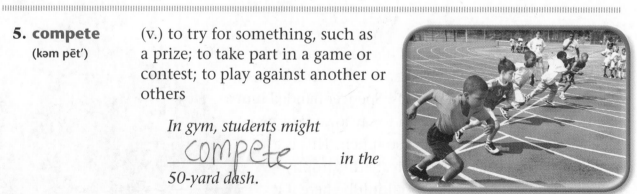

6. consider
(kən sid′ ər)

(v.) to think about or pay attention to

Be sure to ___*consider*___ your choices carefully.

SYNONYMS: weigh, analyze, evaluate, ponder, study
ANTONYMS: decline, reject, repel

7. delightful
(di līt′ fəl)

(adj.) very pleasing, wonderful

Going to a carnival is a ___*delightful*___ experience.

SYNONYMS: lovely, appealing, enjoyable, agreeable, pleasant, joyful
ANTONYMS: disagreeable, displeasing, unpleasant, joyless

8. honor
(ä′ nər)

(n.) great respect; a sign of respect; a sense of what is right

They sent a card in ___*honor*___ of my birthday.

(v.) to respect or value

We should ___*honor*___ our teachers.

SYNONYMS: (n. & v.) praise, credit, esteem; (n.) glory, recognition, privilege
ANTONYMS: (n. & v.) disgrace, dishonor; (v.) humiliate

9. reflex
(rē′ fleks)

(n.) an automatic response, usually very quick

My ___*reflex*___ is to jump at the sight of a spider.

SYNONYM: instinct

10. remark
(ri märk′)

(n.) a short statement

That was an unkind ___*remark*___ about their old shoes.

(v.) to say, mention; give an opinion

Ask them to ___*remark*___ on the shape of the clouds.

SYNONYMS: (n. & v.) comment; (n.) observations; (v.) observe, speak, state, mention

Match the Meaning

vocabularyworkshop.com
Practice unit words with interactive games and activities.

Choose the word whose meaning is suggested by the clue given.
Then write the word on the line provided.

1. A quick reaction is a(n) _reflex_.
   a. ability   ⓑ reflex   c. honor

2. A person who has the skill to do something has the
   ability to do it.
   ⓐ remark   b. honor   ⓒ ability

3. When I make a(n) _remark_, I am commenting on something.
   ⓐ remark   b. ability   c. honor

4. To _avoid_ something is to stay away from it.
   ⓐ avoid   b. consider   c. compete

5. A _brief_ speech is a short one.
   a. bashful   ⓑ brief   c. delightful

6. People who are afraid to speak up might be _bashful_.
   ⓐ bashful   b. brief   c. delightful

7. To _consider_ taking an action is to think about doing it.
   a. compete   ⓑ consider   c. remark

8. To _compete_ in a race is to take part in it.
   a. avoid   b. remark   ⓒ compete

9. A person who is well respected receives much _honor_.
   a. ability   b. reflex   ⓒ honor

10. The long vacation was enjoyable and _delightful_.
    ⓐ delightful   b. bashful   c. brief

On this obstacle course, the contestants must **avoid** the cones.

Synonyms

Choose the word that is most nearly the **same** in meaning as the word or phrase in **dark print**. Then write your choice on the line provided.

1. **escape** the bad weather
   a. compete   b. consider   c. avoid

   avoid

2. **strive** for the first place
   a. consider   b. compete   c. remark

   compete

3. a **shy** newcomer
   a. bashful   b. brief   c. delightful

   bashful

4. a nasty **comment**
   a. honor   b. remark   c. reflex

   remark

5. **study** the test results
   a. avoid   b. compete   c. consider

   consider

6. a quick **response**
   a. ability   b. reflex   c. remark

   reflex

Antonyms

Choose the word that is most nearly **opposite** in meaning to the word or phrase in **dark print**. Then write your choice on the line provided.

1. a **lengthy** conversation
   a. brief   b. bashful   c. delightful

   brief

2. a **disagreeable** situation
   a. brief   b. delightful   c. bashful

   delightful

3. **humiliate** the person
   a. avoid   b. honor   c. remark

   honor

4. an **inability** to understand
   a. honor   b. ability   c. reflex

   ability

Completing the Sentence

Choose the word from the box that best completes each item below. Then write the word on the line provided. (You may have to change the word's ending.)

ability	avoid	bashful
brief	compete	consider
delightful	honor	
reflex	remark	

My Pets

■ My parents often _____ on how well I take care of my dog and cat, saying that I treat my pets very well.

■ Each of my pets has different _____. A talent that my cat has is the ability to react and move quickly. She can do

that because she has great _____.

■ My cat is sometimes _____. At times, she hides from strangers, the way a shy child might.

■ I love to watch my dog play with other dogs. It's

fun to watch the dogs _____ for a big bone or a ball, bumping into each other as each one tries to get the object.

■ Once in a while, I come home from school and am very tired. I'm just not in the mood to play with my dog and cat! On

those days, I almost feel like _____ my pets.

■ But I always make sure to spend some time with them. Even a

_____ amount of time with them is better than no time at all!

■ I love my cat and dog. They are both charming and _____.

It is a(n) _____ to have them as pets!

■ Which animal do you _____ to be the better pet? You have to decide that for yourself!

Word Study • Analogies 1

An **analogy** is a statement that shows how two pairs of words are related. It is usually in the following form: _____ is to _____ as _____ is to _____.

Look at the examples at the right. In Example 1, *bashful* (page 90) and *bold* are antonyms. To complete this analogy, find another pair of words that are antonyms. Answer *b*, *restless* and *relaxed*, are also antonyms. Here is the complete analogy: *bashful* is to *bold* as *restless* is to *relaxed*.

In Example 2, *remark* (page 91) and *comment* are synonyms. Answer *b*, *grasp* is to *cling*, completes the analogy: *remark* is to *comment* as *grasp* is to *cling*.

Example 1
Antonyms
bashful is to *bold* as
  a. *fast* is to *quick*
  b. *restless* is to *relaxed*

Example 2
Synonyms
remark is to *comment* as
  a. *throw* is to *catch*
  b. *grasp* is to *cling*

PRACTICE *Complete each analogy with the missing word. Write the number of the analogy next to the word that best completes it.*

1. *shatter* is to *break* as *wander* is to   _____ *foolish*

2. *honor* is to *respect* as *harm* is to   _____ *hurt*

3. *gentle* is to *rough* as *wise* is to   _____ *short*

4. *damp* is to *wet* as *brief* is to   _____ *roam*

APPLY *Complete each analogy with a word from the box. Then write whether the words in both pairs are synonyms or antonyms.*

> ancient   depart   reject
> reveal   truthful

5. *freeze* is to *boil* as *hide* is to _____   _____

6. *strong* is to *weak* as *recent* is to _____   _____

7. *wash* is to *clean* as *leave* is to _____   _____

8. *remember* is to *forget* as *accept* is to _____   _____

9. *fair* is to *just* as *honest* is to _____   _____

 Speak   *Create an analogy using a word from Units 7–9. Have a partner complete the analogy. Talk about the relationship between the words.*

Vocabulary for Comprehension

Read the following passage in which some of the words you have studied in Units 7–9 appear in dark print. Then answer the questions on page 97.

Pants as Good as Gold

I'm so glad I left New York for California. Most people came here to make their fortunes mining gold, but not me. I came to start my own business. I am not a **timid** man! I am not afraid to try new things. In New York, my family sold dry goods. I was confident that I would be successful doing the same in California. Most people would be busy looking for gold. I would have few dry goods merchants to **compete** with.

When I arrived in 1853, I opened my business and named it after myself, Levi Strauss. I sold goods to the small stores where miners bought supplies. My business has grown. I have moved several times to bigger locations.

In 1872, big became huge. I got a letter from a tailor named Jacob Davis. He had a **clever** idea. Davis attached metal rivets to pants at the places where they stretch and pull. The rivets **performed** an important job. They made the pants stronger and last longer.

That made me think. I had often heard miners **remark** that their pants wore out too quickly. Most pants are just too **delicate** for digging for gold! So when Davis asked for my help, I agreed to join him. I knew that many miners would want these sturdy work pants.

Now I am proud when I see miners wearing denim pants with rivets. I like to hear them say their pants are both long lasting and comfortable. I intend to keep making these extraordinary pants. Who would have thought that pants would be as good as gold?

The rivets in the new design meant pants didn't wear out quickly.

Fill in the circle next to the choice that best completes the sentence or answers the question.

1. This passage is mostly about
- (a) Strauss's journey out West.
- (b) how Strauss got rich from making pants.
- (c) why people looked for gold.
- (d) miners in California.

2. The meaning of **timid** is
- (a) bold.
- (b) silent.
- (c) not have courage.
- (d) slow to decide.

3. Strauss would have few merchants to **compete** with because
- (a) most people would be looking for gold.
- (b) his family sold dry goods in New York.
- (c) he named his business after himself.
- (d) the merchants sold few supplies.

4. Another word for **clever** is
- (a) strong.
- (b) slow.
- (c) smart.
- (d) strange.

5. In this passage, **performed** means
- (a) carried out a task.
- (b) entertained.
- (c) made.
- (d) punched with holes.

6. The meaning of **remark** in this passage is
- (a) to question.
- (b) to wonder.
- (c) to do again.
- (d) to make a statement.

7. **Delicate** most nearly means
- (a) sturdy.
- (b) weak.
- (c) fancy.
- (d) small.

8. You can figure out that Strauss
- (a) missed his family.
- (b) wanted to dig for gold.
- (c) made friends easily.
- (d) was proud of his success.

Write Your Own

The pants that Levi Strauss and Jacob Davis made led to the many different kinds of blue jeans in stores today. Think about the effect of Strauss and Davis's creation. On a separate sheet of paper, describe how their creation affects us today. Use at least three words from Units 7–9.

Introducing the Words

Read the following fairy tale about an unusual test that a princess must pass. Notice how the highlighted words are used. These are the words you will be learning in this unit.

The Princess and the Pea

(Fairy Tale)

Once upon a time, there was a rich, handsome prince. He was also a man of great wit and charm. Many maidens tried to conquer his affection. Often, they pretended to be princesses! It had all become very frustrating. The prince would only marry a true princess.

One day, the prince was hunting in the woods. Suddenly, he saw a maiden on the brink of a cliff. She was crying softly.

"What is wrong, dear lady?" he asked.

"I wandered off from my royal party and am lost," she said.

"Are you a princess?"

"Of course!" she snapped. "What do you intend to do to help me?"

Before he could answer, the wind blew fiercely. A loud clap of thunder shook the forest. The fury of the storm made it impossible to speak. The prince helped the maiden onto his horse and took her back to his castle.

By the time they reached the castle, the maiden felt a chill. Her cloak was wet, and her teeth were chattering. The prince's servants brought hot soup. Then one of them handed the young woman a fresh gown with patterns of polka dots and stripes.

The maiden shrieked. "A princess can't wear this! I must have velvet!"

So the servant brought her a velvet gown. The maiden said, "I wish to sleep now."

The prince thought, "She acts like royalty, but is she an actual princess? I must find out."

The young woman was led up to a tower. Twenty mattresses were placed one on top of the other. The top mattress was covered with a quilt made with vibrant patches of color. A pea was placed under the mattress at the very bottom of the pile. The maiden climbed a ladder to the top and got into bed.

The next morning, the prince entered the tower.

The maiden said, "I must apologize for my behavior yesterday. I was fortunate to have been saved from the storm. I am grateful for your help."

"How did you sleep, dear lady?" the prince asked.

The maiden said, "I hate to complain, but I slept very poorly! There is something hard under the bed!"

"So you are a princess! Will you marry me?"

"I don't think so," she said. "You couldn't tell that I was a princess."

"Many maidens have tried to fool me. I had to put you to the test. You felt the pea under the twenty mattresses. Only a real princess would be so delicate. Wouldn't you prefer someone who could truly judge your royal upbringing?"

The princess softened. After they got to know one another, she agreed to marry him. They lived happily ever after, and the princess never again slept with a pea under her mattress.

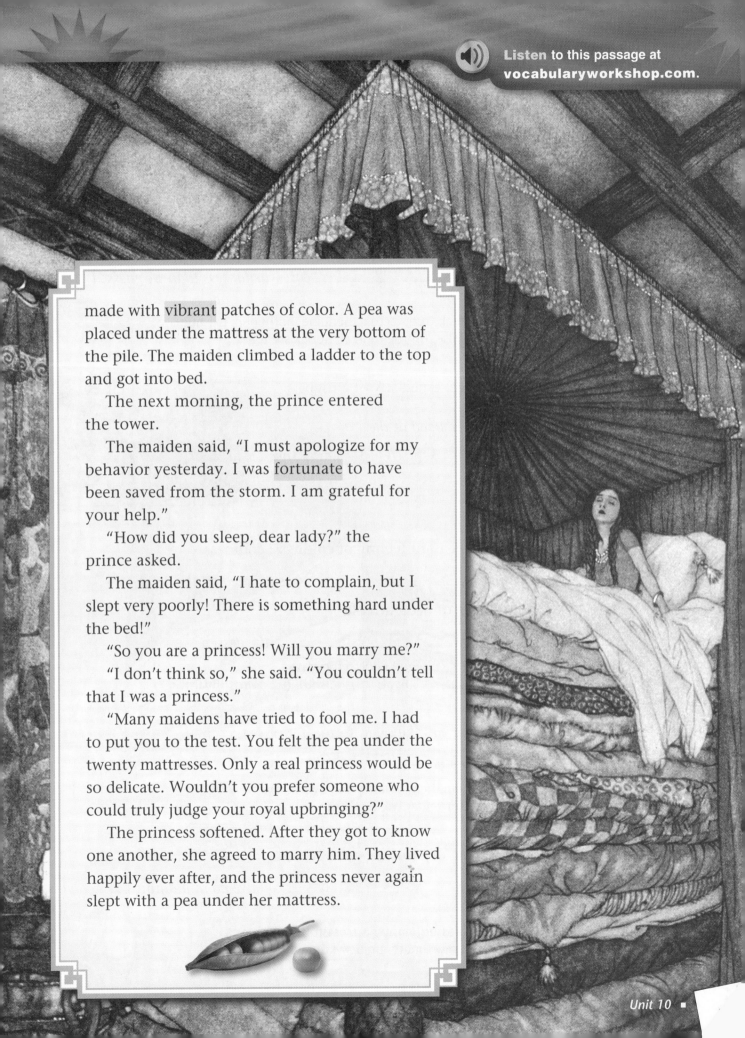

Definitions

You were introduced to the words below in the passage on pages 98–99. Study the spelling, pronunciation, part of speech, and definition of each word. Write the word on the line in the sentence. Then read the synonyms and antonyms.

1. actual
(ak′ chü wəl)

(adj.) happening in fact or reality

The _actual_ cost was far less than we guessed it would be.

SYNONYMS: real, true, factual, genuine, authentic, existing
ANTONYMS: false, untrue, unreal, nonexistent

2. brink
(briŋk)

(n.) the edge, especially of a high, steep place

The hiker stood at the _brink_ of the cliff.

3. chill
(chil)

(n.) an unpleasant feeling of coldness; coolness

I felt a _chill_ as I skated on the pond.

(v.) to make or become cold

Should we _chill_ the dessert?

SYNONYMS: (n.) nip; (v.) cool, refrigerate
ANTONYMS: (n. & v.) heat; (n.) warmth; (v.) defrost; warm

4. conquer
(kän′ kər)

(v.) to defeat or take over; to master or overcome

The army hoped to _conquer_ the enemy quickly.

SYNONYMS: win, beat, overpower, overthrow
ANTONYMS: surrender, yield, submit, relinquish

5. fortunate
(fôr′ chə nət)

(adj.) having or bringing good luck; lucky

We were _fortunate_ to have no rain during spring break.

SYNONYMS: blessed, happy, successful, favorable
ANTONYMS: unfortunate, unlucky, unfavorable

6. fury
(fyùr′ ē)

(n.) strong anger, rage
A bad temper often leads to a state of
fury.

SYNONYMS: wrath, fierceness, violence, force, power

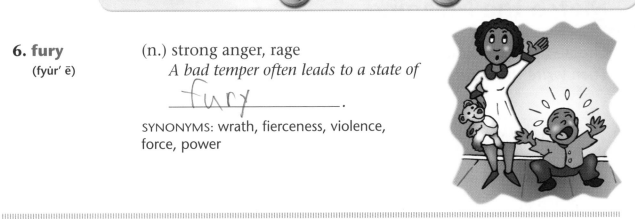

7. intend
(in tend′)

(v.) to plan to do something; to have a goal or purpose
I hope you _intend_ *to do your homework.*

SYNONYMS: plan, mean, aim, expect, propose

8. pattern
(pat′ ərn)

(n.) the way that shapes and colors are put together; a model or guide for making something; a design that is repeated
The striped _pattern_ *is the same in each candy cane.*

(v.) to make or follow according to a model or design
I hope to _pattern_ *my behavior after someone I look up to.*

SYNONYMS: (n. & v.) style, form; (n.) system, order, arrangement, sequence, standard; (v.) imitate, match

9. vibrant
(vī′ brənt)

(adj.) full of life, energy, or activity
Your personality is lively and _vibrant_.

SYNONYMS: lively, energetic, spirited, dynamic, vivid, bright, striking
ANTONYMS: lifeless, dull, ordinary, unremarkable

10. wit
(wit)

(n.) the talent to describe things or people in a funny or unusual way; the ability to think clearly; a clever and amusing person
A teacher with _wit_ *often knows how to keep the students' attention in class.*

SYNONYMS: humor, intelligence, cleverness

Match the Meaning

vocabularyworkshop.com
Practice unit words with interactive games and activities.

Choose the word whose meaning is suggested by the clue given.
Then write the word on the line provided.

1. A _____ is a design that repeats.
   a. wit   b. brink   c. pattern

2. Something that is true or real is _____.
   a. actual   b. vibrant   c. fortunate

3. You might look over the _____ of a riverbank to look for fish.
   a. brink   b. chill   c. fury

4. A funny person is also sometimes called a
   _____wit_____.
   a. pattern   b. wit   c. brink

5. When you make something cold, you
   _____chill_____ it.
   a. conquer   b. pattern   c. chill

6. Something _____ is full of life.
   a. actual   b. vibrant   c. fortunate

7. If you are _____, you have good luck.
   a. actual   b. fortunate   c. vibrant

8. To overcome a problem is to _____ it.
   a. conquer   b. chill   c. intend

9. A very angry person might show _____.
   a. brink   b. pattern   c. fury

10. To _____ to complete a project is to plan to finish it.
    a. chill   b. conquer   c. intend

The woman had to **conquer** her fear of heights before skydiving.

Synonyms

Choose the word that is most nearly the **same** in meaning as the word or phrase in **dark print**. Then write your choice on the line provided.

1. hang over the **edge**
   a. fury   b. brink   c. pattern   _____

2. the tiger's **rage**
   a. wit   b. chill   c. fury   _____

3. showing great **intelligence**
   a. brink   b. wit   c. pattern   _____

4. a gorgeous **design**
   a. pattern   b. chill   c. fury   _____

5. **plan** to see us
   a. intend   b. chill   c. conquer   _____

Antonyms

Choose the word that is most nearly **opposite** in meaning to the word or phrase in **dark print**. Then write your choice on the line provided.

1. an **unreal** event
   a. vibrant   b. actual   c. fortunate   _____

2. **warm up** the dessert
   a. chill   b. conquer   c. pattern   _____

3. an **unlucky** person
   a. actual   b. vibrant   c. fortunate   _____

4. **surrender** the territory
   a. conquer   b. pattern   c. intend   _____

5. a **dull** story
   a. actual   b. fortunate   c. vibrant   _____

Completing the Sentence

Choose the word from the box that best completes each item below. Then write the word on the line provided. (You may have to change the word's ending.)

actual	brink	chill
conquer	fortunate	fury
intend	pattern	
vibrant	wit	

Books

■ I read every book the same way. My reading _____ is to find a book, put my feet up, and turn to the first page.

■ I like reading biographies because I know that I am reading the

_____ facts of a person's life.

■ I love authors who put _____ into their stories and make me laugh out loud.

■ Some mystery books are so good that reading them

can send _____ up my spine.

■ The books that I enjoy most are those that are fun

to read and have a _____ writing style.

■ My favorite author is Roald Dahl. I like *James and the Giant Peach* so

much that I _____ to read it again.

Water, Water Everywhere

■ One way that people have tried to _____ the endless flow of rivers is to build dams, levees, and reservoirs.

■ Scientists stand at the _____ of a cliff to observe the flow of the river below.

■ People who live in areas of high rainfall are

_____. They are lucky that they never have to worry about getting enough water.

■ There is nothing that compares with the

_____ of a hurricane.

Word Associations

*Circle the letter next to the choice that best completes the sentence or answers the question. Pay special attention to the word in **dark print.***

1. A story of **actual** events is about
   a. made-up events.
   b. events that never happened.
   c. real events.
   d. aliens or robots.

2. "I **intend** to go bowling" means
   a. I never want to bowl.
   b. I plan to try bowling.
   c. I'm afraid to try bowling.
   d. I don't know what bowling is.

3. If the Bugs **conquer** the Bees, you can say that
   a. the Bugs win.
   b. the Bees win.
   c. the Bugs lose.
   d. it's a tie game.

4. A **vibrant** poem is one that
   a. always rhymes.
   b. sounds like all the others.
   c. is exciting.
   d. is boring.

5. One way to **chill** a drink is to
   a. add ice cubes to it.
   b. boil it for five minutes.
   c. sprinkle salt into it.
   d. pour it into a jar.

6. A song with **wit** might make you
   a. cry.
   b. laugh.
   c. forget the words.
   d. cover your ears.

7. Which comment shows **fury**?
   a. "What a tasty dessert!"
   b. "Sweet dreams, dear."
   c. "That's a beautiful sweater!"
   d. "Wait till I give them a piece of my mind!"

8. We stood at the **brink** of the cliff
   a. to enjoy the view.
   b. to eat lunch.
   c. to get out of the storm.
   d. to fly a kite.

9. You'd probably feel **fortunate** if
   a. you got caught in the rain.
   b. you scraped your knee.
   c. you found a $10 bill.
   d. you lost your wallet.

10. A dress with a **pattern** has a
    a. long zipper.
    b. repeating design.
    c. shiny belt.
    d. roomy pocket.

Word Study • Prefixes *un-*, *de-*, *over-*

You have learned that a **prefix** is a word part that is added to the beginning of a **base word** to make a new word.

Look at the prefixes and base words in this chart. The prefix *un-* means "not." You can add *un-* to *fortunate* (page 100) to make the word *unfortunate*. *Unfortunate* means "not fortunate."

Prefix	Base Word	New Word	Meaning
un + fortunate	=	**un**fortunate →	not fortunate
de + frost	=	**de**frost →	remove frost or ice
over + flow	=	**over**flow →	beyond the top

The prefix *de-* often means "remove." The prefix *over-* means "too much" or "beyond." Look at the chart for examples of words with the prefixes *de-* and *over-*.

PRACTICE *Write the missing prefix or base word. Then write the meaning of the new word.*

Prefix	Base Word		New Word	Meaning
1. _____ +	safe	=	unsafe →	_____
2. over +	_____	=	overtime →	_____
3. _____ +	plane	=	deplane →	_____
4. un +	_____	=	uncertain →	_____

APPLY *Complete each sentence with a word that contains the prefix* un-, de-, *or* over-. *Choose from the words in the boxes above.*

5. During a thunderstorm, it is _____ to be outside.

6. I took the turkey out of the freezer to _____ it.

7. The worker got paid for _____ after working extra hours this week.

8. The passengers on Flight 24 will _____ at City Airport.

 Add the prefix un-, de-, *or* over- *to each word below to make a new word. Then write a sentence for each new word. You may use a dictionary if you need help.*

value   **happy**   **eat**

Shades of Meaning • Idioms 2

In the passage "The Princess and the Pea" on pages 98–99, you read this sentence about the prince: *He was also a man of great **wit** and charm*. In this sentence, the word *wit* means "being clever when using words or ideas."

An **idiom** is an expression with a special meaning. You cannot figure out its meaning from the individual words. Here is an example: *So many answers on the test looked right that the girl was **at her wit's end***. Here, the idiom *at her wit's end* doesn't refer to clever words or ideas. Instead, it tells how the girl feels. *At her wit's end* means "so upset that she does not know what to do." Below are some idioms that express how we think or feel.

PRACTICE *Read each sentence. Figure out the meaning of each idiom in **dark print**. Write the number of the sentence next to the meaning of the idiom.*

1. I feel **tongue-tied** when I begin an oral report, but I start to relax as I speak.

2. I have been **on top of the world** since I won the spelling contest.

3. I was **on the edge of my seat** every time our team got close to scoring a point.

4. I wanted to ride the roller coaster, but I had **second thoughts** when I saw how big it was.

_____ interested in a way that makes you excited and nervous

_____ having problems expressing yourself because you are nervous

_____ doubts about a decision you have made

_____ feeling wonderful or very happy about something

APPLY *Read each sentence. Figure out the meaning of each idiom in **dark print**. Write the meaning on the line provided.*

5. I had **my heart set** on going to the street fair until it rained.

_____

6. My brother looked **down in the mouth**, but he wouldn't tell me what was wrong.

_____

7. Mom promised to **keep an open mind** as I told her how I wanted to decorate my room.

_____

Introducing the Words

Read the following journal article about a shipwreck that was found hundreds of years after it was lost at sea. Notice how the highlighted words are used. These are the words you will be learning in this unit.

Treasure Among Diamonds

(Journal Article)

In March 1533, a ship named *Bom Jesus* sailed from Lisbon, Portugal. It was headed for India. At the time, Portugal was in its full glory as a rich and powerful nation. Its kings and queens sent ships to trade in faraway places.

It was a tradition to celebrate when a ship sailed. Flags waved in the harbor. Castles displayed colorful banners. In this way, people waved good-bye to the crew of the *Bom Jesus*.

Gold coins were found in the *Bom Jesus* wreckage.

This map shows the journey of the *Bom Jesus*.

After leaving Lisbon, the ship approached the Atlantic Ocean. It was carrying a magnificent load of gold and copper for trading. Pieces of these metals would be traded for rare spices such as pepper and cloves. Later, the spices could be sold for a lot of money.

In those days, ship travel was not for the meek or easily frightened sailor. Danger was always near. Storms could arise. Ships could split apart on rocks. From 1525 to 1600, twenty-one ships bound for India were lost at sea.

Four or five months after leaving Lisbon, the *Bom Jesus* was approaching the tip of Africa. Suddenly, a wild storm pushed the ship toward the shore. The ship struck rocks. All that was on board spilled into the sea. The *Bom Jesus* sank out of sight. Hundreds of years later, diamonds were discovered in the African country of Namibia. The discovery happened to take place near the rocks where the *Bom Jesus* had sunk. Now a company had opened a diamond mine at the site.

In 2008, a mine worker found an oddly shaped piece of copper on the beach. He took it to the mine company's geologist. The geologist, a scientist who studies the earth, recognized the piece. It was an ingot, a block of copper. He knew it would have been traded for spices long ago.

The geologist also knew that if there was a copper ingot, there was a good chance that a shipwreck was nearby. He described the findings to scientists who searched for shipwrecks. However, since the diamond-mining company owned the beach, the mine owners had to approve any plan for a search.

The response of the mine owners was prompt. They agreed that scientists could look for the ship's wreckage. However, they would only give the searchers ten weeks. Also, the owners would be watchful to make sure no diamonds disappeared from the beach. That meant examining each shipwreck item before it was removed from the site.

The scientists believed that the ship was the *Bom Jesus*. Their guess turned out to be right. By the end of their search, they had uncovered 50 pounds of gold. They found 22 tons of copper ingots. They discovered cannons, swords, guns, and ivory. A wooden part of the ship was recovered, too. All these treasures helped to tell the story and revive the memory of people who sailed the sea so long ago.

Definitions

You were introduced to the words below in the passage on pages 108–109. Study the spelling, pronunciation, part of speech, and definition of each word. Write the word on the line in the sentence. Then read the synonyms and antonyms.

1. approach
(ə prōch′)

(v.) to come close to; to begin to deal with; to make a request

We watched the brand new train __approach__ *the station.*

(n.) the act of coming close to; a way to deal with something or someone; a way of reaching a place

The __approach__ *of spring makes many people giddy.*

SYNONYMS: (v. & n.) access; (v.) near; undertake; (n.) manner, method, technique, attitude, style; entrance, avenue
ANTONYMS: (v.) leave, avoid, retreat

2. approve
(ə prüv′)

(v.) to have a high opinion of; to give permission

My parents __approve__ *of my loyal friends.*

SYNONYMS: accept, admire; agree to, endorse, authorize
ANTONYMS: reject, condemn, disapprove

3. glory
(glôr′ ē)

(n.) great honor or praise given by others; great beauty

Can anything match the __glory__ *of a sunset?*

SYNONYMS: fame; splendor, magnificence
ANTONYMS: shame, disgrace, dishonor; ugliness

4. magnificent
(mag ni′ fə sənt)

(adj.) very grand and fine; remarkably beautiful or outstanding

The Taj Mahal in India is a __magnificent__ *building.*

SYNONYMS: superb, majestic, striking, splendid, glorious, impressive
ANTONYMS: ordinary, plain, simple, modest, poor

5. meek
(mēk)

(adj.) not courageous or strong

I felt _meek_ and did not speak loudly enough.

SYNONYMS: mild, gentle, quiet; weak, timid
ANTONYMS: strong, courageous, brave, bold, outgoing, outspoken, aggressive

6. prompt
(prämpt)

(adj.) on time; done quickly and without delay

They answered the invitation in a _prompt_ manner.

(v.) to move someone to action; to remind someone what to do or what to say

I had to _prompt_ my friend to make the call.

SYNONYMS: (adj.) early, punctual, timely; fast, quick; (v.) cause, make, urge, encourage, motivate, cue
ANTONYMS: (adj.) slow, late, tardy, delayed; (v.) discourage, deter

7. revive
(ri vīv')

(v.) to bring or come back to life

The nurse tried to _revive_ the patient.

SYNONYMS: resuscitate, renew, restore
ANTONYMS: deaden, impair, kill

8. tradition
(trə di' shən)

(n.) a custom, belief, or idea that has been passed down over time

Celebrating with a Fourth of July parade is a _tradition_ in many towns and cities.

SYNONYMS: pattern, practice, ritual

9. watchful
(wäch' fəl)

(adj.) always noticing what is happening, aware

A scout must be silent and _watchful_.

SYNONYMS: alert, observant, vigilant
ANTONYMS: sleepy, unaware, oblivious

10. wreckage
(re' kij)

(n.) what is left of something that has been destroyed

The _wreckage_ of the car was taken away.

SYNONYMS: ruins, remains, remnants, destruction

Match the Meaning

Choose the word whose meaning is suggested by the clue given.
Then write the word on the line provided.

1. A ____mag____ object might also be described as splendid.
    a. meek   **b. magnificent**   c. prompt

2. When you give an okay to a job, you _____ it.
    a. revive   b. approach   **c. approve**

3. To lack courage is to be _____.
    a. watchful   **b. meek**   c. magnificent

4. A(n) _____ to a highway brings you close to it.
    a. wreckage   b. glory   **c. approach**

5. The remains of an explosion are often called

_____.
    a. wreckage   b. approach   c. glory

6. A(n) _____ is a custom that is passed down.
    a. approach   **b. tradition**   c. glory

7. To _____ someone is to bring that person back to life.
    a. approve   b. approach   **c. revive**

The cat kept a **watchful** eye on the bird.

8. To be _____ is to be awake and alert.
    a. watchful   b. prompt   c. magnificent

9. People who are _____ are known to be on time.
    a. magnificent   b. watchful   **c. prompt**

10. Those who want great honor may want a lot of _____.
    a. glory   b. tradition   c. wreckage

Synonyms

Choose the word that is most nearly the **same** in meaning as the word or phrase in **dark print**. Then write your choice on the line provided.

1. **resuscitate** the patient
   a. approach
   b. approve
   c. revive ⟵

   revive

2. a family **ritual**
   a. wreckage
   b. approach
   c. tradition ⟵

   tradition

3. **near** the finish line
   a. approach ⟵
   b. revive
   c. approve

   approach

4. give **praise** to the winner
   a. glory ⟵
   b. approach
   c. wreckage

   glory

5. **endorse** the new test
   a. approach
   b. revive
   c. approve ⟵

   approve

6. clean up the **ruins**
   a. glory
   b. wreckage ⟵
   c. tradition

   wreckage

Antonyms

Choose the word that is most nearly **opposite** in meaning to the word or phrase in **dark print**. Then write your choice on the line provided.

1. a **simple** gown
   a. meek
   b. magnificent ⟵
   c. prompt

   magnificent

2. a **strong** reaction to the insult
   a. watchful
   b. meek ⟵
   c. magnificent

   meek

3. a **sleepy** guard
   a. magnificent
   b. prompt
   c. watchful ⟵

   watchful

4. **discourage** the decision
   a. prompt ⟵
   b. glory
   c. tradition

   prompt

Completing the Sentence

Choose the word from the box that best completes each item below. Then write the word on the line provided. (You may have to change the word's ending.)

> approach   approve   glory
> magnificent   meek   prompt
> revive   tradition
> watchful   wreckage

Ancient Rome

■ The Roman gods received much ___glory___ and honor because they were believed to have incredible powers and strengths.

■ No expense was spared in building the ___magnificent___ temples where these gods were honored.

■ The destruction of Rome resulted in the ___wreckage___ of these temples. Today we see only their ruins.

■ It would not be a good idea to ___revive___ the ancient Roman custom of having gladiators fight lions in coliseums.

■ The Spanish custom of bullfighting is modeled after that early Roman ___tradition___.

School Lunch

■ Our teachers do not ___glory___ of bad manners in the cafeteria.

■ They are ___watchful___ of us as we carry our trays to our tables. They want to make sure there are no accidents and that no child gets hurt.

■ In the rush to get in line for the hot lunch, ___prompt___ children often end up being the last to get their food.

■ Today, our class was the first class to ___approach___ the doors of the cafeteria. That put us at the beginning of the line.

■ Students who are ___meek___ and finish their lunch on time get to go outside for recess.

Word Associations

*Circle the letter next to the choice that best completes the sentence or answers the question. Pay special attention to the word in **dark print**.*

1. If you **approve** of the restaurant, it is likely that you will
   a. hate the food you order.
   b. like the food you order.
   c. argue with the waiter.
   d. argue over the bill.

2. In a quarrel, a **meek** child might
   a. make strong arguments.
   b. refuse to give in.
   c. yell and scream.
   d. not speak up at all.

3. A **magnificent** hotel would have
   a. lumpy beds and broken chairs.
   b. fancy rooms and a grand lobby.
   c. small, plain guest rooms.
   d. poor guest service.

4. You might see **wreckage** after
   a. the street cleaners come.
   b. you mow the lawn.
   c. a building is torn down.
   d. you go to the movies.

5. **Prompt** guests will probably be
   a. angry.
   b. annoying.
   c. on time.
   d. delayed.

6. It is an old **tradition** in our school to have
   a. a field day every June.
   b. teachers in the classroom.
   c. windows in every room.
   d. a telephone number.

7. As I **approach** the lake, it
   a. appears to be farther away.
   b. is harder to see.
   c. seems smaller.
   d. appears to be closer.

8. To **revive** an old car, you must
   a. make it run again.
   b. call an ambulance.
   c. learn to drive.
   d. sell it.

9. A **watchful** clerk
   a. chats with customers.
   b. daydreams a lot.
   c. doesn't notice much.
   d. pays close attention.

10. One **glory** of nature is a
    a. muggy night.
    b. rainbow.
    c. dust storm.
    d. mosquito bite.

Word Study • Suffixes -ness, -er, -or

You have learned that a **suffix** is a word part that is added to the end of a **base word** to make a new word.

Look at the base words and suffixes in this chart. The suffix *-ness* usually means "a state of being." You can add the suffix *-ness* to *prompt* (page 111) to make the word *promptness*. *Promptness* means "the state of being on time."

Base Word	Suffix	New Word	Meaning
prompt + **ness**	= promptness →	the state of being on time
teach + **er**	= teacher →	someone who teaches
act + **or**	= actor →	someone who acts

The suffixes *-er* and *-or* mean "someone who does." Look at the chart for examples of words with the suffixes *-er* and *-or*.

PRACTICE *Write the missing base word or suffix. Then write the meaning of the new word.*

Base Word	Suffix	New Word	Meaning
1. _____	+ er	= painter →	_____
2. kind	+ _____	= kindness →	_____
3. invent	+ _____	= inventor →	_____
4. _____	+ ness	= greatness →	_____

APPLY *Complete each sentence with a word (or words) that contains the suffix -ness, -er, or -or. Choose from the words in the boxes above.*

5. My favorite _____ is performing in the new play.

6. The _____ will display his paintings in the museum.

7. When our neighbors helped us with the gardening, we thanked them for their _____.

8. When I arrived on time for class, my _____ looked at the clock and praised my _____.

 Write *Continue the chart in Practice. List more words with the suffixes -ness, -er, and -or. Write the meaning of each new word.*

Shades of Meaning • Words That Describe People 2

In the passage "Treasure Among Diamonds" on pages 108–109, you read this sentence: *In those days, ship travel was not for the **meek** or easily frightened sailor.* The word *meek* tells the reader that only very daring sailors could endure such trips.

When you describe a person, it is important to use words that give your reader or listener a picture of the person. Look at the words in the chart. They all can be used to describe a person.

aloof	If someone is **aloof**, that person is not very warm or friendly toward other people. The person does not become involved.
bold	If someone is **bold**, that person is not afraid to do things that involve risk or danger.
meek	If a person is **meek**, that person is gentle and mild in manner. The person is likely to do what other people say.

PRACTICE *Write the word from the chart that best describes each kind of person.*

1. My friend does everything her sister tells her to do. _____

2. The newcomer didn't care to join in any conversations. _____

3. The student spoke out in support of the unpopular class president.

   _____

4. Our new neighbor showed no interest in helping to plan the block party.

   _____

APPLY *Think about a person you know who fits each description. Describe the person. Explain how he or she fits the description.*

5. aloof _____

_____

6. bold _____

_____

7. meek _____

_____

Introducing the Words

Read the following folktale about a clever tiger's promise. Notice how the highlighted words are used. These are the words you will be learning in this unit.

The Tiger's Promise

(Korean Folktale)

Long ago, a tiger roamed in the area of a small village. The people were terribly frightened. They put up signs that read, "Watch out for the tiger!" The warnings were punctuated with large exclamation points.

However, the signs didn't do much good. The tiger remained in the area, and everyone was afraid to go outside. The villagers decided it would be better to try to prevent attacks by trapping the tiger. They dug a deep hole and covered it with branches. Sure enough, the tiger fell in and couldn't get out.

The next day, a young man heard a barely audible cry. He looked down into the hole and saw the tiger weeping quietly.

"What's wrong?" the young man asked.

"Woe is me!" said the tiger. "I fell into this hole. If I were a bird, I could fly out. If I were a snake, I could glide away through a tunnel. I am neither of these animals, so I am trapped. Please help me get out!"

The young man was kind, but he was not a fool. He said, "I can't help you—you'll eat me."

"Not true!" the tiger said. "Help me, and I'll return the favor to you someday." Meanwhile, his stomach rumbled with hunger.

The young man lowered a log into the hole. The tiger used it to climb out. When he reached the top, he said, "Hello, breakfast!"

"Wait!" the young man said. "You promised."

"You were foolish to believe that," the tiger said with scorn. "Now I'm afraid I will have to consume you."

A skinny ox was grazing nearby. The young man called out to him. "Kind ox, do you think it's fair for the tiger to eat me?"

The ox looked up from his meal. He said, "As a representative of all the beasts that spend their lives working, I would say it is quite fair. People have done nothing but take advantage of oxen since the origin of humankind. Just look at me—I should be stout and well rested, but instead I am lean and always tired."

Just then a small rabbit hopped by.

The now desperate young man said, "Please, Rabbit, what do you think? I helped the tiger out of the hole. Now he wants to eat me."

The rabbit said to the young man and the tiger, "Show me how this happened."

The young man removed the log from the hole. The tiger, anxious to eat his meal, jumped into the hole.

The tiger said, "You see, I was here and . . ."

". . . there you will stay!" Rabbit said. He turned to the young man. "And you, young man, think twice before you rescue another tiger. A tiger *never* keeps a promise!"

Definitions

You were introduced to the words below in the passage on pages 118–119. Study the spelling, pronunciation, part of speech, and definition of each word. Write the word on the line in the sentence. Then read the synonyms and antonyms.

1. audible
(ô′ də bəl)

(adj.) capable of being heard

The music was _____ down the street.

SYNONYMS: loud, clear, distinct
ANTONYMS: inaudible, faint, indistinct

2. consume
(kən süm′)

(v.) to eat or drink, especially in large amounts; to use up; to destroy

We plan to _____ an early dinner.

SYNONYMS: devour; deplete, waste

3. glide
(glīd)

(v.) to move smoothly and easily

I watched the speed skater _____ around the rink.

SYNONYMS: slide, coast, cruise, sail

4. origin
(ôr′ ə jən)

(n.) the cause or beginning

The _____ of chocolate is the cacao bean.

SYNONYMS: start, source, root, ancestry
ANTONYMS: end, finish, death

5. prevent
(pri vent′)

(v.) to stop from happening

Waterproof boots _____ feet from getting wet.

SYNONYMS: bar, block, prohibit, restrain, obstruct
ANTONYMS: allow, permit, encourage

6. punctuate
(puŋk' chü wāt)

(v.) to mark printed or written materials with periods, commas, and other signs; to give importance to

Be careful how you _____ your sentences.

SYNONYMS: emphasize, accentuate

7. representative
(rep ri zen' tə tiv)

(n.) a typical example; someone who acts for another

She was the company's _____ at the meeting.

(adj.) having to do with elected members; being a typical example

That painting is _____ of pop art.

SYNONYMS: (n.) type; agent, spokesperson, delegate; (adj.) elected, chosen; typical
ANTONYMS: (adj.) atypical, unrepresentative

8. scorn
(skôrn)

(n.) a feeling that something or someone is worthless or inferior; an expression of that feeling

It is not right to treat those who are less fortunate with

_____ .

(v.) to act with contempt toward an object or a person; to make fun of

I wish they did not _____ my old bicycle.

SYNONYMS: (n. & v.) ridicule; (n.) disrespect, mockery; (v.) mock, sneer, dismiss; ANTONYMS: (n.) admiration, praise; (v.) approve, embrace

9. stout
(staút)

(adj.) large and heavy in build; physically strong and sturdy; having courage or determination

The _____ old maple stood in the meadow.

SYNONYMS: fat; brave, bold, courageous
ANTONYMS: cowardly, timid; weak; thin

10. woe
(wō)

(n.) great sorrow or suffering; trouble

I felt such _____ when my poor dog died.

SYNONYMS: sadness, unhappiness, misery, grief; misfortune, suffering
ANTONYMS: happiness, joy; luck

Match the Meaning

vocabularyworkshop.com
Practice unit words with interactive games and activities.

Choose the word whose meaning is suggested by the clue given. Then write the word on the line provided.

1. To _____ is to emphasize.
   a. consume   b. glide   c. punctuate

2. When people feel _____, they feel sadness.
   a. woe   b. scorn   c. representative

3. If you _____ something, you use it up.
   a. glide   b. consume   c. prevent

4. The source of a story is its _____.
   a. woe   b. origin   c. representative

5. When a sound can be heard, it is _____.
   a. audible   b. representative   c. stout

6. To _____ is to move along without much effort.
   a. consume   b. punctuate   c. glide

7. When you sneer at something, you show

   _____ for it.
   a. origin   b. woe   c. scorn

I felt deep woe when I lost my favorite jacket.

8. If you try to _____ something, you are trying to stop it from happening.
   a. prevent   b. consume   c. glide

9. Something that is _____ might also be called sturdy.
   a. audible   b. representative   c. stout

10. A(n) _____ statement is a typical one.
    a. audible   b. representative   c. stout

Synonyms

*Choose the word that is most nearly the **same** in meaning as the word or phrase in **dark print**. Then write your choice on the line provided.*

1. the **root** of their unhappiness
   a. scorn   b. woe   c. origin   _____

2. **cruise** along peacefully
   a. consume   b. prevent   c. glide   _____

3. **emphasize** my remarks
   a. glide   b. prevent   c. punctuate   _____

4. showed terrible **disrespect**
   a. scorn   b. origin   c. woe   _____

5. a **loud** screech
   a. audible   b. stout   c. representative   _____

6. **deplete** your energy
   a. scorn   b. consume   c. glide   _____

Antonyms

*Choose the word that is most nearly **opposite** in meaning to the word or phrase in **dark print**. Then write your choice on the line provided.*

1. was overcome with **joy**
   a. scorn   b. origin   c. woe   _____

2. an **atypical** example
   a. audible   b. stout   c. representative   _____

3. a **cowardly** heart
   a. stout   b. audible   c. representative   _____

4. **allow** the discussion
   a. prevent   b. consume   c. punctuate   _____

Completing the Sentence

Choose the word from the box that best completes each item below. Then write the word on the line provided. (You may have to change the word's ending.)

audible	consume	glide
origin	prevent	punctuate
representative	scorn	
stout	woe	

Astronauts in Space

■ Astronauts looking down on Earth from space can see oceans and land,

but no sounds from our planet are _____.

■ In a spaceship, the astronauts' bodies _____ around smoothly because there is no gravity pulling them down.

■ Astronauts must _____ their food from freeze-dried packets.

■ Even though this food is not very tasty, astronauts

must eat in order to _____ weakness.

Opera

■ The _____ of the term *opera* is the Italian phrase *opera in musica*, meaning "work in music."

■ There are many styles of opera. Therefore, we cannot say that any

one opera is _____ of the musical form.

■ People used to think that opera singers needed to have

bodies that are _____ and strong. However, many opera singers who have powerful voices are actually quite slim.

■ Many operas deal with touching human stories. Often,

a character feels _____ by a loved one. This situation leads to songs that show strong feelings

of _____.

■ Moments of great drama can be _____ by trumpets blaring.

Word Study • Homographs 1

Homographs are multiple-meaning words that have more than one dictionary entry. Homographs are spelled the same but have different meanings. Each entry word is followed by a small raised number.

pound¹	a unit of measure for weight
pound²	to hit hard again and again

The word *pound* is a homograph. Look at the box above to see how *pound* might appear in a dictionary.

Look at the chart for other homographs and their meanings.

bank¹	a place in which money is saved or used for business purposes
bank²	the land, often sloping, along the edge of a river or creek
left¹	relating to the particular side of a person's body
left²	went away from
ring¹	something shaped like a circle
ring²	to make the sound of a bell

PRACTICE *Complete each sentence with a homograph from the chart. Then write the number of the homograph whose meaning is shown.*

_____ **1.** We found a good place to fish along the _____.

_____ **2.** The friends hold hands and form a _____ around the pole.

_____ **3.** He _____ the house early this morning to go to work.

_____ **4.** The camper will _____ the dinner bell at 5 o'clock each day.

_____ **5.** I plan to put my baby-sitting money in the _____.

_____ **6.** She keeps her keys in her _____ pocket.

APPLY *Complete each sentence using words from the chart above.*

7. The guard at the _____ where I keep my money always stands

to the _____ of the safe.

8. Dad wanted to buy the _____ at the jewelry store, but he

realized that he _____ his wallet at home.

 Write a sentence using a word from the charts above. Have your partner tell which meaning of the word fits your sentence.

Vocabulary for Comprehension

*Read the following passage in which some of the words you have studied in Units 10–12 appear in **dark print**. Then answer the questions on page 127.*

A Mountain Hike

Adam gazed at the huge, **magnificent** mountain ahead of him. He **intended** not only to hike to the top but also to camp out there overnight. Although Adam was excited, he was nervous. He had never hiked this far before. He was worried about wild animals, too. What if a bear entered his tent? Adam knew it was important for hikers always to be **watchful**. "I'll have to be aware of my surroundings at all times," Adam said to himself.

His camp counselor's whistle interrupted his thoughts. "Let's get going!" Grace told all ten campers. Adam was determined to **conquer** the challenge. He walked at a brisk pace to keep up with his friends. At first, the trail was flat, so the hike seemed easy. Before long, the group had completed one mile. Grace called for a water break. "The next couple of miles may get harder," she said, "but you can do it!"

Adam was determined. "Nothing will **prevent** me from completing this hike," he thought, "except a bear!" As the hike continued, Adam felt the trail get steeper. His breathing became heavier, too. After a while, Adam was afraid he would need to stop. Just then he heard Grace say, "Here we are!" The group had reached the top of the mountain. Adam realized that he could put aside his worries. He knew now that he could do anything he put his mind to. He also realized that he was so hungry he could **consume** a bear!

Fill in the circle next to the choice that best completes the sentence or answers the question.

1. This passage is mostly about
   a how Adam felt during a hike.
   b what to take on a hike.
   c when Adam completed one mile of the hike.
   d why Adam went on a hike.

2. The meaning of **magnificent** is
   a fun.
   b ordinary.
   c grand.
   d poor.

3. **Intended** most nearly means
   a planned.
   b agreed.
   c worried.
   d considered.

4. Another word for **watchful** is
   a sleepy.
   b alert.
   c careless.
   d simple.

5. The meaning of **conquer** is
   a avoid.
   b forget.
   c overcome.
   d begin.

6. To **prevent** means
   a to allow.
   b to encourage.
   c to beg.
   d to stop.

7. At the end of the story, Adam was
   a disappointed that he didn't finish the hike.
   b sorry that he came on the trip.
   c scared to sleep overnight on the mountain.
   d relieved that he had completed the hike.

8. In this passage, **consume** means to
   a race.
   b eat.
   c scare.
   d buy.

Write Your Own

In this story, Adam battled fear and nervousness, but he eventually met his goal and completed a long hike. Imagine how you would feel if you were in a similar situation. On a separate sheet of paper, tell a story (real or made up) in which you deal with a fear in order to complete a challenge. Use at least three words from Units 10–12.

Classifying

Choose the word from the box that goes best with each group of words. Write the word on the line provided. Then explain what the words have in common.

ancient	bashful	chill
climate	cling	delightful
fortunate		rare
representative		symbol

1. lucky, _____, blessed

_____

2. reserved, _____, friendly, outgoing

_____

3. _____, old, recent, brand-new

_____

4. ring, wing, sting, _____

_____

5. president, senator, governor, _____

_____

6. heat, warm, _____, freeze

_____

7. _____, symbolic, symbolize

_____

8. _____, medium, well-done

_____

9. lovely, pleasant, charming, _____

_____

10. temperature, rainfall, humidity, _____

_____

Completing the Idea

*Complete each sentence so that it makes sense. Pay attention to the word in **dark print**.*

1. One place I would like to **explore** is _____.

2. Life on a **remote** island is likely _____.

3. When I feel scared, my **reflex** is to _____.

4. My favorite shirt has a **pattern** of _____.

5. A kite is able to **glide** freely if _____.

6. It bothers me when people **accuse** me of _____.

7. Mom wants to **revive** our old car because _____.

8. My favorite superhero has the **ability** to _____.

9. The citizens showed **scorn** for the mayor because he _____.

10. It is a **tradition** in my family to _____.

11. The concert was so loud that it was **audible** _____.

12. Please don't **disturb** me when I am _____.

13. A **vibrant** person might _____.

14. If you are not **prompt**, then _____.

15. Many people felt much **woe** after _____.

Writing Challenge

*Write two sentences using the word **coast**. In the first sentence, use **coast** as a noun. In the second sentence, use **coast** as a verb.*

1. _____

2. _____

Introducing the Words

Read the following news article about one of the world's leading sports events. Notice how the highlighted words are used. These are the words you will be learning in this unit.

The Winter Olympics

(News Article)

Every four years, countries from all over the world compete in the Winter Olympics. This competition is all about snow and ice. Opponents race and jump on skis. They fly 90 miles an hour down a track on bobsleds. Snowboarders jump and twist on courses of packed snow. Figure skaters make fantastic jumps and create beautiful arches in their backs as they twirl on the ice.

Athletes go to the Games with great hopes. All yearn to become champions. Some come back home with medals. Others don't win anything. All come back with one thing in common: They have had the experience of being an Olympic athlete.

A Brief History of the Olympic Games

The first Olympic Games took place about three thousand years ago in ancient Greece. The earliest competition was a modest event. The racers ran a short distance on foot—only 210 yards! Later, more races were added. Events in wrestling, jumping, and throwing were also added. Then the Romans conquered Greece, and the Olympic Games eventually disappeared.

In 1896, the first modern Olympics were held. The first Games were the summer Games, but people were already talking about a winter event. In 1924, the first winter Games were held.

The five rings in the Olympic flag represent the five continents.

Listen to this passage at vocabularyworkshop.com.

Snowboarding is a breathtaking sport.

The Modern Winter Olympics

Many changes have come about in the past nine decades of Winter Olympic competition. At first, professional athletes were not allowed to participate. In 1988, an agreement was signed that granted professionals the right to compete. Some of the first professional winter Olympic athletes played on ice hockey teams.

Today, technology helps with the grave responsibilities that come with judging Olympic events. Such technology can clarify who wins and who loses. In skiing and skating, a race can be won by fractions of a second. Today, computers make it easier to determine who wins and by how much. Also, judges may review an event on video. Doing so can help them decide if a first-place finish is valid.

Going for the Gold

In individual competition, the top three finishers of an event each earn a medal. The first place medal is gold. The second place is silver, and the third place is bronze. Today, an authentic gold medal is only part gold. Solid gold medals are too expensive to make. After each event, the top three finishers stand on a platform. Each country's flag is raised. The gold medal winner listens to his or her country's national anthem. Tears may follow. It is an emotional occasion. At that moment, the athlete has been declared the best in his or her sport.

Definitions

You were introduced to the words below in the passage on pages 130–131. Study the spelling, pronunciation, part of speech, and definition of each word. Write the word on the line in the sentence. Then read the synonyms and antonyms.

1. arch
(ärch)

(n.) a curved structure that serves as an opening and as a support

The door to the castle had an _____ over it.

(adj.) main; playful, mischievous

Surprisingly, the _____ enemies joined forces.

SYNONYMS: (n.) archway, curvature, semicircle; (adj.) chief, principal; sly

2. authentic
(ô then′ tik)

(adj.) being the real thing; worthy of belief, true

These are _____ diamonds.

SYNONYMS: actual, genuine; sincere
ANTONYMS: fake, false, counterfeit, inauthentic

3. clarify
(klar′ ə fī)

(v.) to say clearly or make easier to understand

The teacher tried to _____ the assignment.

SYNONYMS: explain, simplify
ANTONYMS: bewilder, complicate, obscure

4. declare
(di klâr′)

(v.) to state strongly; to make a formal or an official statement

I was too shy to _____ my feelings.

SYNONYMS: announce, assert, proclaim
ANTONYM: deny

5. grant
(grant)

(v.) to permit or allow; to admit that something is true

The leader decided to _____ their request.

(n.) something that is given

They received a _____ to study other cultures.

SYNONYMS: (v. & n.) award; (v.) give; allow, concede; (n.) gift, present
ANTONYMS: (v.) refuse, disallow

6. grave
(grāv)

(n.) a hole in the ground where something is buried

The _____ of President Ulysses S. Grant is in New York City.

(adj.) very important and requiring much attention; serious

The climbers were in _____ danger.

SYNONYMS: (n.) tomb; (adj.) critical, significant; solemn, somber
ANTONYMS: (adj.) insignificant, unimportant; cheerful, joking, lighthearted, merry

7. modest
(mä′ dəst)

(adj.) not thinking too highly of oneself, not boastful; proper in speech, dress, or behavior; not extreme or large

We were surprised at how _____ the famous singer was.

SYNONYMS: reserved, humble; simple; moderate
ANTONYMS: bold, conceited, proud, self-assured, vain; excessive, grand

8. opponent
(ə pō′ nənt)

(n.) someone who is set against another, as in a contest, game, argument, or fight

In the sport of fencing, each _____ challenges the other with a special kind of sword.

SYNONYMS: foe, rival, enemy, competitor, challenger
ANTONYMS: ally, partner, helper, friend, teammate

9. valid
(va′ ləd)

(adj.) supported by facts or evidence, true

Your report presents many _____ arguments.

SYNONYMS: convincing, persuasive, sound
ANTONYMS: false, invalid, unconvincing

10. yearn
(yûrn)

(v.) to long for

I _____ for our vacation.

SYNONYMS: desire, wish, want, crave, need, pine, hunger, thirst

Match the Meaning

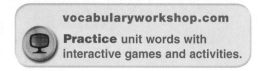
Choose the word whose meaning is suggested by the clue given.
Then write the word on the line provided.

1. The person you are playing against is your _____.
   a. arch   b. opponent   c. grave

2. To want something very much is to _____ for it.
   a. declare   b. yearn   c. clarify

3. An object that is _____ is real and not
   a copy.
   a. grave   b. authentic   c. modest

4. When you make a strong statement, you

   _____ something.

   a. declare   b. arch   c. grant

5. A _____ expression is a serious one.
   a. modest   b. valid   c. grave

6. To allow something to happen is to _____
   it permission to happen.
   a. clarify   b. yearn   c. grant

7. A(n) _____ has a curved shape.
   a. opponent   b. grave   c. arch

8. When you _____ what you say, you make
   it easier to understand.
   a. declare   b. clarify   c. grant

9. A(n) _____ argument is said to be true
   and correct.
   a. valid   b. modest   c. arch

10. A(n) _____ amount is a small amount.
    a. authentic   b. grave   c. modest

**The puppy made the
girl yearn for a pet.**

Synonyms

Choose the word that is most nearly the **same** in meaning as the word or phrase in **dark print**. Then write your choice on the line provided.

1. a frightening **foe**
a. grant   b. arch   c. opponent   _____

2. **pine** for a banana
a. clarify   b. yearn   c. declare   _____

3. a **solemn** event
a. grave   b. arch   c. valid   _____

4. **announce** the winner
a. yearn   b. clarify   c. declare   _____

5. **concede** the favor
a. grant   b. arch   c. clarify   _____

6. a **mischievous** smile
a. authentic   b. modest   c. arch   _____

Antonyms

Choose the word that is most nearly **opposite** in meaning to the word or phrase in **dark print**. Then write your choice on the line provided.

1. **fake** coins
a. arch   b. authentic   c. modest   _____

2. a **false** statement
a. modest   b. valid   c. grave   _____

3. a **vain** gymnast
a. valid   b. authentic   c. modest   _____

4. **complicate** the math lesson
a. clarify   b. declare   c. yearn   _____

Completing the Sentence

Choose the word from the box that best completes each item below. Then write the word on the line provided. (You may have to change the word's ending.)

arch	authentic	clarify
declare	grant	grave
modest	opponent	
valid	yearn	

Baseball

■ A good baseball announcer will _____ the complicated rules of the game.

■ It is the job of the umpire at home plate to _____ whether a pitch is a ball or a strike.

■ It's always nice to find major league players who are _____ and do not like to brag about themselves.

■ All players _____ to play a good game. Of course, they want to beat their _____.

■ That is certainly a _____ goal, but no team can win all the time, no matter how hard the players try.

Museums

■ We saw designs of Greek temples in the museum and learned that the _____ above the doorways can have a point at the top.

■ We also learned that the paintings in the museum are not fake but _____.

■ Many museums offer _____ to students that allow them to study how the artworks were made.

■ Some students even dig up old _____ in ancient cities to learn about people who lived in the past.

Word Associations

*Circle the letter next to the choice that best completes the sentence or answers the question. Pay special attention to the word in **dark print**.*

1. You need to **clarify** rules that
   a. are easy to follow.
   b. are not important.
   c. are complicated.
   d. nobody cares about.

2. People usually have **grave** looks on their faces when they are
   a. at a circus.
   b. at a funeral.
   c. at a brunch.
   d. at a party.

3. Your **opponent** probably wants
   a. to help you.
   b. to feed you.
   c. to lose to you.
   d. to beat you.

4. Which forms a natural **arch**?
   a. a horseshoe
   b. an octopus
   c. a monkey
   d. a brick

5. A **valid** fishing license
   a. is no longer legal.
   b. is impossible to get.
   c. is in effect now.
   d. says that fish are real.

6. An **authentic** Japanese coin
   a. is not real.
   b. comes from Japan.
   c. is made in America.
   d. can be used in America.

7. What might you say when you **grant** my request?
   a. "You may have your wish."
   b. "I won't ever agree to it."
   c. "That is not allowed."
   d. "I will never do anything for you."

8. An actor might **yearn** most for
   a. an old costume.
   b. a leading role.
   c. a broken leg.
   d. a bad performance.

9. A **modest** piece of cake would be
   a. huge.
   b. salty.
   c. small.
   d. chocolate.

10. You **declare** something if you
    a. are just waking up.
    b. are in the middle of a deep sleep.
    c. feel unsure about that thing.
    d. feel strongly about that thing.

Word Study • Compound Words

A **compound word** is a word made by joining two smaller words. You can use what you know about the two smaller words to figure out the meaning of the larger word.

For example, the word *gravestone* is a compound word. It is made up of the smaller words *grave* (page 133) and *stone*. *Gravestone* means "a stone used to mark a grave."

PRACTICE *Find the two words that make up each compound word. Write the words. Then write the meaning of the compound word.*

1. _____ + _____ = lifeboat → _____

2. _____ + _____ = wastebasket → _____

3. _____ + _____ = shipwreck → _____

4. _____ + _____ = roommate → _____

5. _____ + _____ = mailbox → _____

APPLY *Complete each sentence with a compound word. Form the compound word by joining two words from the box.*

board	fall	foot	hand	hold
key	land	made	slide	water

6. We stopped at the edge of the river to admire the _____.

7. I got scared when I spilled water on the _____ of my laptop.

8. I stepped onto the _____ as I climbed the rock wall.

9. My costume was special because it was _____.

10. All the flooding caused a _____ in the nearby hills.

 Use all the smaller words shown on this page to make as many new compound words as you can. Trade your list with a partner. Count how many new words you got altogether.

Shades of Meaning • Word Choice

declare, mutter, admit

In the passage "The Winter Olympics" on pages 130–131, you read this sentence: *At that moment, the athlete has been* **declared** *the best in his or her sport.* The word *declared* is a specific word. It tells you that something has been officially announced or made known.

Words may have similar meanings, but no two words have exactly the same meaning. Look at the words in the chart. They all involve speaking. Notice how the words differ in meaning.

declare	When you **declare** something, you say it officially or formally.
mutter	When you **mutter** something, you say it so people can barely hear you. You usually mutter if you are unhappy or complaining.
admit	When you **admit** something, you tell the truth and confess.

PRACTICE *Write the word from the chart that best replaces* **say** *in each sentence.*

1. I think I heard him **say**, "I'm really tired of waiting here." _____

2. It pleases me to **say** that the park is now open to the public! _____

3. I'm sorry to **say** that I was the one who broke the window. _____

4. It wasn't nice to **say** to yourself during the concert that you disliked the songs.

_____

APPLY *Decide how you would speak in each situation. Be prepared to explain your answers.*

5. You broke your friend's new game by accident when he or she wasn't looking. Do you **admit** or **mutter** what you have done? Write what you would say.

_____

6. You are tired of being called by your nickname, which you think you've outgrown. Would you **admit** or **declare** that it is time for people to use the name you want to go by? Write what you would say.

_____

Introducing the Words

Read the following biography about a pioneer of the air. Notice how the highlighted words are used. These are the words you will be learning in this unit.

Amelia Earhart
1897–1937
(Biography)

Surely, no one in Amelia Earhart's family would have predicted that she would one day fly an airplane. Young Amelia showed no interest in airplanes. She was, on the other hand, interested in women who did admirable things. She collected newspaper articles about women who were engineers and lawyers. In the 1920s, it was unusual for females to have such careers.

Years later, people would read about Earhart herself. Her devotion to flying would one day make her famous.

Earhart's interest in flying was kindled by an exciting experience she had as a young woman. She had gone to an air show. At one point, Earhart heard a distant hum and looked up. A small red airplane

Some of the planes Earhart flew are now at the
Air and Space Museum in Washington, DC.

was heading straight toward her and a friend. The plane flew so close that it blew Earhart's hair out of place. She was thrilled.

When Earhart was twenty-three, she flew on her first airplane. A year later, she took her first flying lesson. Six months after that, she bought an airplane.

In 1928, Earhart got a phone call. The man on the line wanted her to be the first woman to fly across the Atlantic Ocean. Was she interested? Earhart didn't have to think twice. An automatic reply of "Yes!" flew out of her mouth.

Two men flew the plane. Earhart made history just by being a passenger. That flight gave her an idea, though: Why couldn't she be the first woman to pilot the same route? In 1932, she achieved her goal. She became the first woman to fly a plane across the Atlantic.

In 1931, Earhart married George Putnam. As she became more famous, she flew more often. Putnam supported Earhart's passion for flying. He didn't mind the long separations that the trips caused. His support helped her try new things.

In 1935, she achieved her next goal. She flew across the Pacific Ocean alone. This flight was 2,408 miles long and would exhaust anyone. Yet Amelia was determined. At one point during the flight, the weather was dreary and cold. To warm herself, she opened a thermos of hot chocolate. She later told people that it was a special moment. There she was, sipping hot chocolate as she flew alone over the middle of the Pacific Ocean!

Amelia Earhart set many world records in aviation.

In 1937, Earhart planned another trip. No other woman had flown around the world yet. She wanted to be the first! She hoped that this stunt would be her last. Sadly, it did become her final trip. Somewhere over the Pacific Ocean, Amelia Earhart's airplane disappeared.

No one knows for sure what happened. She might have crashed in the ocean or on an island. Whatever occurred, Amelia Earhart has a place in history. Today, she is a symbol of courage and adventure.

Definitions

You were introduced to the words below in the passage on pages 140–141. Study the spelling, pronunciation, part of speech, and definition of each word. Write the word on the line in the sentence. Then read the synonyms and antonyms.

1. admirable
(ad' mə rə bəl)

(adj.) deserving praise

The murals they painted on the wall are

_____.

SYNONYMS: excellent, superior, wonderful, praiseworthy, first-rate
ANTONYMS: inferior, mediocre, second-rate

2. automatic
(ô tə ma' tik)

(adj.) done without thought or will; done by a machine, not by a human

Blinking is an _____ response.

SYNONYMS: involuntary, instinctive, unconscious, mechanical
ANTONYMS: deliberate, conscious, voluntary

3. devotion
(di vō' shən)

(n.) loyalty and affection

They showed their _____ to their religious faith by attending services on a regular basis.

SYNONYMS: attachment, commitment, dedication, faith, allegiance
ANTONYMS: disloyalty, faithlessness

4. distant
(dis' tənt)

(adj.) far away; not friendly

The _____ cabin was difficult to get to.

SYNONYMS: remote, apart, removed, separated; reserved, unapproachable, unfriendly, cold
ANTONYMS: near, close, adjacent, neighboring; accessible, warm

5. dreary
(drir' ē)

(adj.) gloomy or dismal; without cheer, comfort, or enthusiasm

The rain did not stop at all during the _____ afternoon.

SYNONYMS: depressing, bleak
ANTONYMS: cheery, exciting, vibrant, lively, merry

6. exhaust
(ig zôst′)

(v.) to use up; to wear out

Don't _____ yourself shopping at the mall.

(n.) the escape of gas from an engine

The _____ from the bus made me choke.

SYNONYMS: (v.) tire, fatigue, weaken, consume, deplete, drain, empty
ANTONYMS: (v.) refresh, enliven, fill, quicken

7. kindle
(kin′ dəl)

(v.) to get a fire going; to stir up or to start something

We tried to _____ a campfire.

SYNONYMS: ignite, burn, light; awaken, excite
ANTONYMS: extinguish; discourage, dampen, smother, deaden

8. predict
(pri dikt′)

(v.) to guess what is going to happen

No one can _____ the future.

SYNONYMS: forecast, foretell, foresee, anticipate, expect

9. separation
(se pə rā′ shən)

(n.) the act or condition of being apart

They met again after a _____ of ten years.

SYNONYMS: disconnection, detachment, rift, break, division
ANTONYMS: connection, attachment, unification

10. stunt
(stunt)

(v.) to stop or slow down the growth of

The scientist worked to _____ the growth of the weed.

(n.) an act that shows great strength, bravery, or skill, often to get attention

Harry Houdini, the great magician and escape artist, was known to perform a daring escape

_____.

SYNONYMS: (v.) block, hamper, suppress, restrain;
(n.) feat, performance, achievement
ANTONYMS: (v.) encourage, promote

Match the Meaning

Choose the word whose meaning is suggested by the clue given.
Then write the word on the line provided.

1. To _____ is to make a guess about what will happen.

    a. kindle   b. stunt   c. predict

2. Something _____ might be described as excellent.

    a. automatic   b. distant   c. admirable

3. A feat that displays much skill is a(n) _____.

    a. devotion   b. stunt   c. exhaust

4. Something far away is _____.

    a. admirable   b. automatic   c. distant

5. A(n) _____ reaction is one that happens without thought.

    a. admirable   b. dreary   c. automatic

6. To show _____ is to show loyalty.

    a. devotion   b. separation   c. stunt

7. A(n) _____ from people might also be a detachment from them.

    a. exhaust   b. devotion   c. separation

8. A(n) _____ afternoon can also be considered gloomy.

    a. distant   b. dreary   c. automatic

9. To light a fire is to _____ it.

    a. predict   b. kindle   c. stunt

10. The fumes that come from an engine are called _____.

    a. separation   b. material   c. exhaust

The guide dog showed complete devotion to the man.

Synonyms

Choose the word that is most nearly the **same** in meaning as the word or phrase in **dark print**. Then write your choice on the line provided.

1. tire out the workers

a. exhaust   b. kindle   c. predict   _____

2. forecast the weather

a. kindle   b. exhaust   c. predict   _____

3. hamper your progress

a. kindle   b. exhaust   c. stunt   _____

4. an **excellent** way with animals

a. automatic   b. admirable   c. distant   _____

5. an **involuntary** thought

a. automatic   b. admirable   c. dreary   _____

Antonyms

Choose the word that is most nearly **opposite** in meaning to the word or phrase in **dark print**. Then write your choice on the line provided.

1. a long **attachment**

a. devotion   b. separation   c. stunt   _____

2. a **cheery** scene

a. admirable   b. automatic   c. dreary   _____

3. extinguish the flame

a. kindle   b. stunt   c. exhaust   _____

4. a soldier's **disloyalty**

a. stunt   b. separation   c. devotion   _____

5. a **close** relative

a. admirable   b. distant   c. automatic   _____

Completing the Sentence

Choose the word from the box that best completes each item below. Then write the word on the line provided. (You may have to change the word's ending.)

admirable	automatic	devotion
distant	dreary	exhaust
kindle	predict	
separation	stunt	

Winter

■ Many people find the long, cold winter to be _____.

■ It helps the mood to _____ a fire and warm up by the fireplace.

■ Winter sports can also help a person's frame of mind. It can be fun to ice skate for hours, even if it

_____ you!

■ Sometimes, however, the winter seems as if it will never end. Spring seems to be a

_____ dream.

My Friend, the Gardener

■ I have a friend who is an _____ gardener. Everything he plants grows beautifully.

■ The _____ he shows to every detail of his garden is impressive.

■ He's always happy when the weather forecasters

_____ rain. That is because he knows that if it doesn't rain, the plants' growth

will be _____ by lack of water.

■ When he goes away, he turns on an _____ sprinkler that will water his garden in his absence.

■ If you want my friend to be happy, make sure there is never too long

a _____ between him and his garden!

Word Associations

*Circle the letter next to the choice that best completes the sentence or answers the question. Pay special attention to the word in **dark print**.*

1. To show **devotion** to learning,
   a. come late to class.
   b. do your homework.
   c. forget to study.
   d. skip school.

2. If you seem **distant** to someone,
   a. you are warm.
   b. you are cold.
   c. you are friendly.
   d. you are happy.

3. You might see daring **stunts** at the
   a. computer.
   b. hardware store.
   c. grocery store.
   d. circus.

4. If you feel **exhausted**, you might
   a. jog a few miles.
   b. paint a picture.
   c. take a nap.
   d. learn to skate.

5. A long **separation** would be
   a. a lot of time to wait.
   b. a little time to wait.
   c. something to look forward to.
   d. something you probably wouldn't notice.

6. It's an **admirable** trait to be
   a. polite.
   b. grumpy.
   c. selfish.
   d. boring.

7. On a dark and **dreary** Saturday afternoon, you might feel
   a. excited.
   b. gloomy.
   c. honored.
   d. hopeful.

8. You can **predict** the score for
   a. last night's ball game.
   b. yesterday's ball game.
   c. tomorrow's ball game.
   d. last week's ball game.

9. Which of these things would you use to **kindle** a fire?
   a. water
   b. soda
   c. plastic
   d. matches

10. Which of the following is done **automatically**?
    a. driving
    b. eating
    c. drinking
    d. breathing

Word Study • Homographs 2

You have learned that **homographs** are multiple-meaning words that have separate entries in a dictionary. Homographs have a small raised number after them in the dictionary.

exhaust[1]	to use up or wear out
exhaust[2]	the escape of gas from an engine

The word *exhaust* (page 143) is a homograph. Look at the box above to see how *exhaust* would appear in a dictionary.

Look at the chart for other homographs and their meanings.

bear[1]	to support or carry; to last through something
bear[2]	a large, furry mammal with a short tail
shed[1]	a small shelter
shed[2]	to drop or throw off
fine[1]	high quality
fine[2]	money paid as punishment

PRACTICE *Complete each sentence with a homograph from the chart. Write the number of the homograph whose meaning is shown.*

____ **1.** A _____ may eat both plants and insects.

____ **2.** A snake will _____ its skin.

____ **3.** I couldn't _____ the weight of my backpack any longer.

____ **4.** Late library books mean you must pay a _____.

____ **5.** The graduation gown was made of very _____ cloth.

____ **6.** Dad's tools are kept in the _____.

APPLY *Complete each sentence using words from the chart above.*

7. I hid in the _____ to avoid the prowling _____.

8. Dad couldn't _____ to pay the $50 _____.

9. The dog _____ its hair on Mom's _____ carpet.

Write *Write a sentence that includes a pair of homographs.*

Example: My mother **set** her best **set** of dishes on the table.

Shades of Meaning • Word Choice
predict, suspect, wonder

In the passage "Amelia Earhart" on pages 140–141, you read this sentence: *Surely, no one in Amelia Earhart's family would have **predicted** that she would one day fly an airplane*. When people predict, they make a guess about what will happen in the future. They are not certain of the outcome.

When you know something for sure, you are certain about it. When you don't know something for sure, there are words that can describe your level of understanding. The chart below shows some of these words.

predict	When you **predict**, you say what is going to happen based on what you already know.
suspect	When you **suspect**, you believe something is probably true based on clues.
wonder	When you **wonder**, you think about something that you want to know more about.

PRACTICE *Write the word from the chart that best completes each sentence.*

1. I _____ a deer was here because I see its footprints.

2. As you read, _____ what will happen at the end of the story.

3. I _____ why the bus driver is late in picking us up.

4. I _____ that it is going to rain tomorrow.

5. We _____ that a raccoon got into the garbage last night.

APPLY *Answer each question. Use the word in **dark print** in your answer. Be sure to write complete sentences.*

6. What is something in nature that you **wonder** about?

_____

7. What do you **predict** you will be doing at this hour next week?

_____

8. What do you **suspect** happened to Amelia Earhart?

_____

Introducing the Words

Read the following magazine article about an underwater wonderland. Notice how the highlighted words are used. These are the words you will be learning in this unit.

The Great Barrier Reef

(Magazine Article)

Dive into the waters of northeastern Australia, and you will find the Great Barrier Reef. This natural wonder runs along the coast like a colorful underwater fence. You will see picturesque structures made of coral. Corals are made up of tiny sea creatures that have clumped together. They are often white, pink, or reddish. Some corals are shaped like fans. Others look like the horns of a deer or moose. Still others look like flowers.

Perhaps you will have the privilege of seeing the reef from an airplane. This sight is equally stunning. You can see islands of coral in the clear, blue-green water.

Reefs keep growing in size. The Great Barrier Reef, which has been forming for millions of years, is about 1,400 miles long.

Life on the reef is abundant. It is home to more than 1,500 kinds of fish. Hiding near the coral are tiny fish that have bodies you can see through. Deadly stonefish stare at divers with fierce eyes. Sea turtles, clownfish, and dolphins also swim in the waters.

Fish like to find nooks and crannies within the reef. There, they can slumber in safety. They must stay hidden because the barrier reef is a hunting ground.

Sharks, stonefish, and manta rays are just a few of the predators that search for food in these waters.

In recent years, scientists have noticed changes in the Great Barrier Reef. They have inquired about how human activities might be affecting it. Money was set aside. Then formal tests were run. The tests showed that the reef is no longer growing.

The scientists believe that the pollution of the air and land are two reasons behind the changes. Rain carries dangerous substances into ocean waters. It also washes chemicals that pollute the land into the ocean. These chemicals harm the reefs, which need clear, clean water to survive.

Another problem might be the warming temperatures. Corals grow in warm oceans. However, if the water is too warm, they die.

The Great Barrier Reef took a long time to form. To save the reef from destruction, the Australian government has passed laws to protect it. Anyone who knowingly breaks these laws will be penalized. In addition, scientists all over the world are putting their ideas together. Before long, they might conceive more ways to protect this natural treasure.

Definitions

You were introduced to the words below in the passage on pages 150–151. Study the spelling, pronunciation, part of speech, and definition of each word. Write the word on the line in the sentence. Then read the synonyms and antonyms.

1. abundant
(ə bun′ dənt)

(adj.) large or more than enough; plentiful

There was an _____ amount of food at the restaurant.

SYNONYMS: bountiful, generous
ANTONYMS: limited, meager, sparse, scarce

2. barrier
(bar′ ē ər)

(n.) something that blocks or bars movement or passage

The mountains acted as a _____ to the wind.

SYNONYMS: wall, obstacle, barricade, roadblock, obstruction, restraint
ANTONYMS: entrance, passageway

3. conceive
(kən sēv′)

(v.) to start something; to think up or begin to understand

I began to _____ a plan on how to get all my work done.

SYNONYMS: form, formulate, develop, devise, imagine, think

4. formal
(fôr′ məl)

(adj.) following strict rules or customs; requiring fancy clothes and fine manners

The club members were required to follow a

_____ dress code.

SYNONYMS: official, conventional, standard; proper, fancy
ANTONYMS: informal, unofficial; casual

5. inquire
(in kwīr′)

(v.) to ask about

The detective has begun to _____ about the crime.

SYNONYMS: investigate, question, examine, explore, interrogate

6. penalize
(pē' nəl īz)

(v.) to punish

Our teacher will _____ us for incomplete work.

SYNONYMS: discipline, chasten
ANTONYM: reward

---

7. picturesque
(pik chə resk')

(adj.) charming, quaint

The little town is so

_____.

SYNONYMS: beautiful, pretty, lovely, striking, vivid, scenic, delightful
ANTONYMS: ugly, drab, dull, grim, unpleasant, distasteful

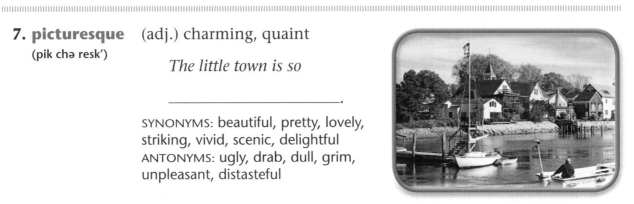

---

8. predator
(pre' də tər)

(n.) one that destroys or devours others; an animal that stalks and eats other animals

A snake is a _____ of mice and other rodents.

SYNONYMS: thief, bandit
ANTONYMS: prey, victim

---

9. privilege
(priv' lij)

(n.) a special right, benefit, or permission

The players who arrived first got the _____ of choosing the nicest uniforms.

SYNONYMS: advantage, honor

---

10. slumber
(slum' bər)

(v.) to sleep lightly

The baby will _____ for a while after lunch.

(n.) a sleep or light sleep

The cat lay in _____ for most of the afternoon.

SYNONYMS: (v. & n.) nap, doze, rest, snooze
ANTONYMS: (v.) awake, arouse, stir; (n.) awareness

Match the Meaning

Choose the word whose meaning is suggested by the clue given.
Then write the word on the line provided.

1. A _____ blocks the way or does not allow passage.
   a. barrier   b. privilege   c. slumber

2. To _____ is to give a punishment or penalty.
   a. conceive   b. slumber   c. penalize

3. An invitation to a(n) _____ party might request that you dress in a fancy way.
   a. formal   b. abundant   c. picturesque

4. If you fall asleep, you are said to

   _____.

   a. penalize   b. inquire   c. slumber

5. To think of a plan or an idea is to

   _____ it.

   a. inquire   b. conceive   c. penalize

6. A _____ is known to attack and eat its prey.
   a. predator   b. privilege   c. barrier

7. When you _____ about a story, you ask about it.
   a. inquire   b. slumber   c. conceive

The bald eagle is a skilled **predator** because of its sharp eyesight.

8. An amount that is _____ is large.
   a. formal   b. abundant   c. picturesque

9. An advantage or right can also be known as a _____.
   a. predator   b. barrier   c. privilege

10. The colorful scene was described by the artists as _____.
    a. formal   b. abundant   c. picturesque

Synonyms

Choose the word that is most nearly the **same** in meaning as the word or phrase in **dark print**. Then write your choice on the line provided.

1. a sneaky **bandit**
a. privilege   b. predator   c. barrier   _____

2. the **right** to leave
a. predator   b. privilege   c. slumber   _____

3. a huge **obstacle**
a. barrier   b. predator   c. privilege   _____

4. **ask** about my test score
a. penalize   b. slumber   c. inquire   _____

5. **think of** a clever solution
a. conceive   b. penalize   c. slumber   _____

Antonyms

Choose the word that is most nearly **opposite** in meaning to the word or phrase in **dark print**. Then write your choice on the line provided.

1. caused me to **awake**
a. penalize   b. inquire   c. slumber   _____

2. a **drab** city
a. formal   b. abundant   c. picturesque   _____

3. the **meager** number of birthday cards
a. formal   b. abundant   c. picturesque   _____

4. **reward** the last player remaining in a game
a. conceive   b. inquire   c. penalize   _____

5. a **casual** invitation
a. abundant   b. formal   c. picturesque   _____

Completing the Sentence

Choose the word from the box that best completes each item below. Then write the word on the line provided. (You may have to change the word's ending.)

abundant	barrier	conceive
formal	inquire	penalize
picturesque	predator	
privilege	slumber	

Etymology

■ When we study the history of a word, or its etymology, we learn of its beginnings and how it has come to be a part of our language.

■ The word _____, which we use to describe something that bars the way, comes from the French word *barre*. Dancers use a barre to stretch their legs.

■ A pretty scene is _____. This word comes from *pictor*, the Latin word for painter.

■ Many English words are the result of the joining of two or more Latin words. For example, _____ comes from *privus*, the word for "private," and *lex*, the word for "law."

■ The English word _____, which means "to ask about," comes from the Latin word *quaerere*, which means "to seek."

■ Both the English word _____ and its ancient relative *praedator*, come from the Latin word, which means "to seize or capture."

Skiing

■ I went skiing last week. There was a blizzard the night before, which left a(n) _____ amount of snow.

■ It was hard to _____ how I would make it all the way down the steep mountain without falling!

■ Since that was hard to imagine, I decided to try an easier slope. No one would _____ me for being cautious.

■ Some ski outfits were so fancy that they made skiing seem as if it were a _____ event!

■ At the end of the day, we fell into a peaceful _____ by the fire.

Word Study • Analogies 2

You have learned that an **analogy** is a statement that shows how two pairs of words are related. The words may be synonyms or antonyms. The words may also show other types of relationships.

Here is an analogy with the word *barrier* (page 152): *barrier* is to *block* as *bridge* is to *connect*. In this analogy, the first word in each pair names an object, and the second word gives a function, or a use, for the object. A *barrier* can be used to *block* off an area, and a *bridge* can be used to *connect* two places separated by water.

The chart at the right shows some types of relationships that analogies can have.

Object/ Function	*barrier* is to *block* as *bridge* is to *connect*
Synonym	*slumber* is to *nap* as *draw* is to *sketch*
Antonym	*formal* is to *casual* as *picturesque* is to *ugly*

PRACTICE *Match the word pairs to form a complete analogy. Write the number of the first pair next to the pair with the same relationship.*

1. *small* is to *tiny* as _____ *thin* is to *lean*

2. *crayon* is to *color* as _____ *leader* is to *follower*

3. *friend* is to *enemy* as _____ *needle* is to *sew*

APPLY *Complete each analogy with a word from the box. Then explain the relationship on the lines provided.*

> chop   fly
> notice   vibrant

4. *gloomy* is to *cheerful* as *dull* is to _____

Relationship: _____

5. *knife* is to *cut* as *axe* is to _____

Relationship: _____

6. *sprint* is to *dash* as *observe* is to _____

Relationship: _____

7. *car* is to *drive* as *plane* is to _____

Relationship: _____

 With a partner, create an analogy using a word from Units 10–15. Talk about the relationship between the words.

Vocabulary for Comprehension

*Read the following passage in which some of the words you have studied in Units 13–15 appear in **dark print**. Then answer the questions on page 159.*

An Amazing Creature

The coast of Florida is home to many turtle nests during warm summer months. Turtles nest along ocean beaches in other southern states, too. Loggerheads are one type of turtle that nest on the beach.

A loggerhead can grow to be as long as three feet. Some may weigh as much as 350 pounds or more. These huge creatures spend most of their lives in the ocean. They swim for years at a time. When a loggerhead female is ready to lay eggs, though, she journeys to a **distant** beach. Usually, she returns to the beach where she was born.

On the beach, the female digs a hole in the sand. She lays about 100 eggs inside. She buries the eggs so **predators** cannot find them. Then she returns to the sea. A month or two later, the young turtles are born. They crawl out of the sand, and their **separation** from the sea is over. They immediately make their way to the ocean. The young turtles are only about two inches long.

Loggerhead nests used to be **abundant**. But now they are in **grave** danger. When people build houses on the beach, loggerheads stay away. In addition, bright lights from the houses confuse the turtles, causing them to run in the wrong direction—away from the ocean. As a result, fewer loggerheads are being born or survive than in the past. Scientists worry that these turtles may die out.

Some people want the government to **declare** the loggerhead an endangered species. They also want to protect beaches where loggerheads nest. That way, more loggerheads may be born in the future.

Baby loggerhead turtles heading toward the ocean

Fill in the circle next to the choice that best completes the sentence or answers the question.

1. This passage is mostly about
- (a) things you see at the beach.
- (b) animals in Florida.
- (c) loggerhead turtles and their nests.
- (d) how sea turtles swim.

2. In this passage, **distant** means
- (a) far away.
- (b) near.
- (c) easy to reach.
- (d) not friendly.

3. The **predators** in this passage are
- (a) animals that lay turtle eggs.
- (b) scientists who study turtles.
- (c) people who build houses.
- (d) animals that eat turtle eggs.

4. A **separation** from the sea means
- (a) having a connection to it.
- (b) being apart from it.
- (c) being related to it.
- (d) having an interest in it.

5. Another word for **abundant** is
- (a) few.
- (b) happy.
- (c) confused.
- (d) plentiful.

6. The meaning of **grave** is
- (a) reserved.
- (b) serious.
- (c) wonderful.
- (d) remote.

7. Which of these is <u>not</u> true about loggerhead turtles?
- (a) They spend most of their lives on land.
- (b) They lay eggs on the beach.
- (c) They swim a lot.
- (d) They can be very big.

8. In this passage, **declare** means
- (a) to sing.
- (b) to state quietly.
- (c) to make a formal statement.
- (d) to make a complaint.

Write Your Own

Some people worry that loggerhead turtles will die off if their homes are not protected. Think about reasons why the government should help protect the loggerhead. On a separate sheet of paper, write a paragraph that tells the government what it can do to help protect loggerhead turtles. Use at least three words from Units 13–15.

Introducing the Words

Read the following fantasy about a wild adventure. Notice how the highlighted words are used. These are the words you will be learning in this unit.

Two Troublesome Monkeys

(Fantasy)

Barnie and Chichi were monkeys who lived in the rain forest. They were always getting into trouble. They took advantage of the younger monkeys and stole their bananas. They played tricks on the older monkeys.

One day, the monkey troop held a meeting. Chief Monkey announced, "We've had enough of you, Barnie and Chichi."

"What are you implying?" Chichi asked.

"I'm not implying anything!" Chief Monkey said. "I am saying it clearly. You won't listen to anyone and you are defiant. Go and leave us all in peace!"

Now, Chichi had always wanted to travel. "Great," she said. "I am totally ready."

Barnie had always had ambition. He wanted to be Chief Monkey some day. He thought he might be able to learn things from people, so he agreed with Chichi. The two of them caught the next train into the city.

As soon as they got off the train, they saw a bus marked "City Zoo." "Sounds like fun," said Chichi.

Once inside the zoo, they caused nothing but trouble. They made faces at the giraffes, jumped on the backs of two fearsome tigers, and teased the bears. Soon, all of the animals in the zoo were upset and started screeching. The zookeeper said, "I revoke all of your privileges to visit this zoo! You shouldn't have been allowed inside in the first place! I'm calling the police!"

By this time, the two monkeys were hungry and ready to leave anyway. Barnie spotted a police officer buying a banana at a fruit stand. Chichi grabbed the banana. Barnie stole a mango. Then the two monkeys ran off as fast as they could.

By then, the police were on full alert. The officers finally caught the monkeys. Not long after, the monkeys found themselves sitting in jail.

"Have you noticed how dirty the city air is?" Chichi asked.

"Yes," Barnie said, "they should purify it."

"Have you noticed how small and damp this cell is?"

"It's wretched."

"It's noisy here, too," Chichi remarked. "And the banana I ate wasn't ripe. I think we were better off in the rain forest."

"That idea merits further thought," Barnie said.

At that moment, Chief Monkey appeared outside the jail cell. She said, "I'm here to take you home."

"Great!" Chichi and Barnie exclaimed together.

"There's one condition!"

"We're glad to negotiate!" Chichi said. "We don't really like the city."

"Very well," Chief Monkey said. "Then you will cause no more trouble at home. You'll respect both the young and old monkeys."

"We promise!" the two monkeys said.

And so the two monkeys went back to the rain forest. From then on, they were well behaved. In a few years, Chichi, not Barnie, became Chief Monkey. She kept perfect order within the troop. She knew how to deal with troublesome monkeys. After all, she had been one herself.

Definitions

You were introduced to the words below in the passage on pages 160–161. Study the spelling, pronunciation, part of speech, and definition of each word. Write the word on the line in the sentence. Then read the synonyms and antonyms.

1. advantage
(əd van' tij)

(n.) something that puts someone in a better position

The _____ of sitting up front is being able to see the movie better.

SYNONYMS: benefit, gain, edge, asset
ANTONYMS: disadvantage, drawback

2. ambition
(am bi' shən)

(n.) a strong desire for importance or success

My _____ is to be an excellent artist.

SYNONYMS: aim, aspiration, goal

3. defiant
(di fi' ənt)

(adj.) showing strong resistance; willing to challenge or confront

The _____ team member refused to listen to the coach.

SYNONYMS: rebellious, disobedient, uncooperative
ANTONYMS: submissive, cooperative, obedient

4. fearsome
(fir' səm)

(adj.) frightening or alarming

That horror movie was quite _____.

SYNONYMS: scary, terrifying, horrifying
ANTONYMS: reassuring, comforting, encouraging

5. imply
(im plī')

(v.) to suggest something without saying it directly

Their kind remarks _____ that they want me to join in.

SYNONYMS: hint, indicate
ANTONYMS: declare, state, announce

6. merit
(mer′ ət)

(n.) a quality that deserves praise

The chief _____ of the book is its surprise ending.

(v.) to be worthy of, deserve

We _____ good grades for our hard work.

SYNONYMS: (n.) value, virtue, worth, excellence, achievement;
(v.) earn, warrant
ANTONYMS: (n.) inferiority, fault

7. negotiate
(ni gō′ shē āt)

(v.) to discuss in order to arrive at an agreement

The United States and Great Britain

_____ the Treaty of Paris in 1783.

SYNONYM: debate

8. purify
(pyùr′ ə fī)

(v.) to make clean and free of dirt or pollutants

We need to _____ the dirty water so we can drink it.

SYNONYMS: cleanse, filter, freshen, refine, sanitize
ANTONYMS: pollute, contaminate, cloud, dirty, muddy, soil

9. revoke
(ri vōk′)

(v.) to cancel by withdrawing or reversing

The judge decided to _____. his license.

SYNONYMS: remove, repeal, rescind
ANTONYMS: give, offer, provide, supply

10. wretched
(re′ chəd)

(adj.) very unhappy or unfortunate, miserable; very poor in quality

We felt _____ about the terrible accident.

SYNONYMS: depressed, dejected; inferior, dreadful
ANTONYMS: happy, pleased, elated, great, superior

Match the Meaning

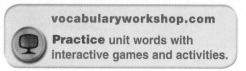
Choose the word whose meaning is suggested by the clue given.
Then write the word on the line provided.

1. To refuse to obey authority is to be _____.
  a. fearsome   b. wretched   c. defiant

2. To have a(n) _____ is to be in a better position
  than others are.
  a. ambition   b. merit   c. advantage

3. When you feel really awful, you feel _____.
  a. fearsome   b. defiant   c. wretched

4. If you _____ water, you make
  it clean.
  a. imply   b. purify   c. negotiate

5. To _____ an offer is to take it back.
  a. merit   b. revoke   c. negotiate

6. A(n) _____ is a wish to achieve or
  be successful.
  a. ambition   b. advantage   c. merit

7. Something that is _____ can also be
  described as scary.
  a. fearsome   b. defiant   c. wretched

8. To _____ is to try to reach
  an agreement.
  a. revoke   b. purify   c. negotiate

The great white shark
is a **fearsome** fish.

9. A job that is well done _____ a reward.
  a. implies   b. merits   c. purifies

10. When you hint at something, you _____ it.
  a. imply   b. merit   c. purify

Synonyms

Choose the word that is most nearly the **same** in meaning as the word or phrase in **dark print**. Then write your choice on the line provided.

1. a **terrifying** howl
a. fearsome   b. defiant   c. wretched   _____

2. a daring **aspiration**
a. ambition   b. advantage   c. merit   _____

3. **discuss** who does the dishes
a. imply   b. negotiate   c. merit   _____

4. **hint** that they are coming
a. revoke   b. merit   c. imply   _____

5. **rescind** the offer
a. purify   b. revoke   c. merit   _____

6. a **virtue** worth rewarding
a. merit   b. advantage   c. ambition   _____

Antonyms

Choose the word that is most nearly **opposite** in meaning to the word or phrase in **dark print**. Then write your choice on the line provided.

1. an unbelievable **handicap**
a. advantage   b. ambition   c. merit   _____

2. **obedient** children
a. fearsome   b. wretched   c. defiant   _____

3. in **superior** condition
a. fearsome   b. wretched   c. defiant   _____

4. **contaminate** the air
a. purify   b. negotiate   c. revoke   _____

Completing the Sentence

Choose the word from the box that best completes each item below. Then write the word on the line provided. (You may have to change the word's ending.)

advantage	ambition	defiant
fearsome	imply	merit
negotiate	purify	
revoke	wretched	

Baking

■ Our family has a tradition of baking a cake every Sunday.

Now it's my _____ to be a professional baker.

■ If we misbehave, our baking privileges are

_____, and our fun is taken away.

■ We use only the best ingredients in our cakes, and

we _____ the tap water by using a water filter.

■ I like banana cake, but my parents prefer carrot cake. We have to

_____ which cake to make.

■ The cake comes out perfectly! It always _____ compliments and praise.

■ I have learned that if we kids _____ that we want a piece of cake, no one will respond. We have to ask for it directly!

Polar Bears

■ Polar bears are aggressive and powerful hunters and can be

quite _____. It is only when

people are _____ and confront a bear that they put themselves in danger.

■ Polar bears live in very cold climates. To us, it

might seem like a _____ way to live, but polar bears love the cold and ice. They

have the _____ of a furry coat to keep them warm.

Word Associations

*Circle the letter next to the choice that best completes the sentence or answers the question. Pay special attention to the word in **dark print**.*

1. A person who is **defiant** might be
a. hungry.
b. sleepy.
c. weak.
d. bold.

2. Which **implies** that you are sad?
a. "I'm not in a very jolly mood."
b. "I feel like I could eat a horse!"
c. "I am floating on air!"
d. "I love fresh fruit."

3. You must **purify** drinking water if it is
a. cold.
b. polluted.
c. fresh.
d. wet.

4. After a long and **wretched** night without sleep,
a. you feel great.
b. you feel rested.
c. you feel tired.
d. you want dinner.

5. A **fearsome** dog may make you
a. bark.
b. growl.
c. tremble.
d. laugh.

6. In summer, it's an **advantage** to
a. have hot soup.
b. have mittens.
c. have a snow suit.
d. have an air conditioner.

7. A movie that has **merit** is likely to
a. be in black-and-white.
b. win an award.
c. come with free popcorn.
d. have actors in it.

8. If your free pass is **revoked**, you
a. may enter without paying.
b. will not be allowed to pay.
c. will have to pay to enter.
d. will have to go home.

9. When people **negotiate**, they expect to
a. sink or swim.
b. laugh or cry.
c. give and take.
d. dance and sing.

10. Someone with strong **ambition**
a. tries to be a failure.
b. tries to be lazy.
c. tries to be a great success.
d. doesn't care about anything.

Word Study • Prefixes *dis-*, *mis-*, *im-*

Remember that a **prefix** is a word part that is added to the beginning of a **base word** to make a new word.

Look at the prefixes and base words in this chart. The prefix *dis-* means "opposite of."

Prefix	Base Word	New Word	Meaning
dis + advantage	= **dis**advantage	→ opposite of advantage
mis + inform	= **mis**inform	→ give wrong information
im + pure	= **im**pure	→ not pure or clean

You can add *dis-* to *advantage* (page 162) to make the word *disadvantage*. *Disadvantage* means "opposite of advantage."

The prefix *mis-* sometimes means "wrongly." The prefix *im-* sometimes means "not." Look at the chart for examples of words with the prefixes *mis-* and *im-*.

PRACTICE *Write the missing prefix or base word. Then write the meaning of the new word.*

	Prefix	Base Word	New Word		Meaning
1.	_____ + polite		= impolite	→	_____
2.	dis + _____		= dislike	→	_____
3.	_____ + use		= misuse	→	_____
4.	mis + _____		= misunderstand	→	_____

APPLY *Complete each sentence with a word that contains the prefix* dis-, mis-, *or* im-. *Choose from the words in the boxes above.*

5. If you _____ the MP3 player, it might stop working.

6. The party guest was _____ to leave without thanking the host.

7. When the star player was absent, the team was at a _____.

8. I don't want to _____ the directions, so I will listen carefully.

Watch out for words that seem to have prefixes but really do not. For example, when you remove im *from* imagine, *no base word remains. In this example,* im *is not a prefix. Underline the words below that do not have a prefix. Explain your choices to a partner.*

distant   disappear   mistrust   mister   impossible   imitate

Shades of Meaning • Words That Describe Behavior

In the passage "Two Troublesome Monkeys" on pages 160–161, you read this sentence: *You won't listen to anyone and you are **defiant**!* In the sentence, *defiant* is used to describe Chichi's behavior. Behavior is the way in which a person or animal acts.

Look at the words in the chart. They each describe a particular behavior.

defiant	A person who is **defiant** is willing to challenge or confront others.
charming	A person who is **charming** has the ability to attract and please people.
cunning	A person who is **cunning** is skilled at tricking others.

PRACTICE *Write the word from the chart that best describes each behavior.*

1. The singer wore sunglasses and a large hat so that she would not be noticed.

_____

2. The actor smiled and shook hands with all of his fans. _____

3. The child would not leave the playground. _____

4. She told a delightful story at the dinner table. _____

5. The thief slipped away quietly as the police arrived. _____

6. The angry crowd refused to be silent during the speech. _____

APPLY *Write about a time when you have shown or seen each behavior.*

7. cunning _____

_____

8. charming _____

_____

9. defiant _____

_____

Introducing the Words

Read the following journal article about an animal that lives near warm bodies of water in Africa. Notice how the highlighted words are used. These are the words you will be learning in this unit.

The Nile Crocodile

(Journal Article)

The Nile crocodile is the largest crocodile in Africa. It is a fearsome animal with huge jaws. It also has large teeth. Its strong body can move quickly.

Habitat

The Nile crocodile lives in the warmer parts of Africa. It must live near water. The animal will die without it. The Nile crocodile might live in tranquil freshwater lakes. It might live in muddy, swampy rivers. It might even live in a ditch. The Nile crocodile sometimes travels as far as 15 miles in search of water.

Nile crocodiles can live for short periods in salt water. Scientists think that at some point, they even swam across the channel that separates Madagascar from Africa. This would explain how this kind of crocodile came to live on Madagascar.

Behavior

The Nile crocodile is a cold-blooded animal. It depends on its surroundings to keep its body warm and cool. To warm up, it lies in the sun to absorb heat. To cool off, it moves into the shade or the water. It also opens its mouth to let heat escape.

Diet

For some crocodiles, waiting in the water for hours for its food might seem tiresome. For the Nile crocodile, however, it's all in a day's work.

Unlike many animals that hunt on land, the Nile crocodile does not target mainly sick, lame, and weak animals. Instead, it waits to attack any animal that comes near. For example, a gazelle, a deerlike animal that moves with grace, might wander over for a drink. Its elegant neck reaches down

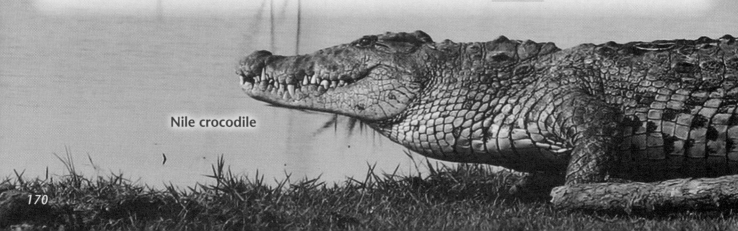

Nile crocodile

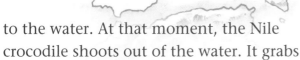

to the water. At that moment, the Nile crocodile shoots out of the water. It grabs the gazelle with its huge jaws.

A Nile crocodile eats almost anything that it can catch. It enjoys fish. It eats small or large land animals. It will even eat other crocodiles!

Description

Most people don't get close enough to a Nile crocodile to inspect it. However, if you could take a close look, you would see strong feet and legs. The tail is very strong, too. It moves the crocodile through the water quickly. The tail is so powerful, in fact, that it can knock down a large animal.

The eyes and nostrils of this crocodile are on the top of its head. This makes it possible for the crocodile to suspend its body under water and still see and breathe.

Tourists travel in boats to see Nile crocodiles. Both professional and amateur photographers have taken photographs of this fierce animal. Wise visitors know they must stay clear of its tail and mouth. If hungry, a Nile crocodile will take a bite out of almost anything . . . or anyone!

NILE CROCODILE FACTS

- **Can weigh over 2,000 pounds**
- **Can measure 20 feet in length**
- **Can eat half its weight in one meal**
- **Can live between 45 and 100 years**
- **Cannot chew. It tips its head up and swallows the food whole!**

Mozambique
Channel

AFRICA

MADAGASCAR

Definitions

You were introduced to the words below in the passage on pages 170–171. Study the spelling, pronunciation, part of speech, and definition of each word. Write the word on the line in the sentence. Then read the synonyms and antonyms.

1. absorb
(əb sôrb')

(v.) to soak up or take in; to keep the attention of

A sponge can _____ every last drop of water.

SYNONYMS: consume, devour; engage, captivate, engross
ANTONYMS: discharge, emit, secrete

2. amateur
(a' mə tər)

(n.) someone who does something for pleasure and not for money; someone who does not have much experience

The young boy wanted to be a professional singer but sang with his

choir as an _____.

SYNONYMS: beginner, nonprofessional, layman
ANTONYMS: expert, professional, master

3. channel
(chan' əl)

(n.) the deepest part of a river; a body of water that links two larger ones; a long, narrow groove; a band of radio waves; a course of action

Many ships pass through the _____between England and France.

(v.) to make a long, narrow groove; to direct or focus

They began to _____ through the rock.

SYNONYMS: (n.) passage, strait, waterway; course, way, direction; (v.) plow, cut; direct, guide

4. elegant
(e' li gənt)

(adj.) showing beauty, high quality, and good taste

The diamond is an _____ jewel.

SYNONYMS: stylish, graceful, exquisite, charming, refined, cultured
ANTONYMS: coarse, crude, inelegant, unfashionable, rough

5. grace
(grās)

(n.) ease and beauty of movement; a charming or pleasing quality; a short prayer at meals

The horse galloped with incredible

_____.

(v.) to add beauty or honor to

Will she _____ our party with her presence?

SYNONYMS: (n.) elegance, loveliness, charm; (v.) enhance, enrich, adorn
ANTONYMS: (n.) clumsiness, inelegance; (v.) disgrace

6. inspect
(in spekt')

(v.) to look over closely

Please _____ the clothes for any damage.

SYNONYMS: examine, check, investigate, probe, scan

7. lame
(lām)

(adj.) stiff, sore, or not able to move properly; weak, not satisfactory

I cannot swim because of my _____ leg.

SYNONYMS: disabled, limping, weak; feeble, flimsy, unconvincing
ANTONYMS: strong, healthy

8. suspend
(sə spend')

(v.) to hang in order to allow free movement; to stop for a time, interrupt; to bar from a position or privilege

Please _____ those streamers from the ceiling.

SYNONYMS: dangle; postpone, delay, halt; remove, exclude
ANTONYMS: continue, resume, prolong

9. tiresome
(tīr' səm)

(adj.) annoyingly dull or exhausting; unexciting

Scrubbing the kitchen floor can be _____.

SYNONYMS: boring, annoying, irritating
ANTONYMS: interesting, exciting, pleasant

10. tranquil
(traŋ' kwəl)

(adj.) free from trouble or disturbance; quiet

The _____ lake is relaxing.

SYNONYMS: calm, serene, peaceful, composed
ANTONYMS: noisy, disturbed, excited

Match the Meaning

Choose the word whose meaning is suggested by the clue given. Then write the word on the line provided.

1. When you stop an activity for a short while, you _____ it.
   a. absorb   b. suspend   c. inspect

2. If you are a beginner, you are a(n) _____.
   a. channel   b. amateur   c. grace

3. An irritating chore can be described as _____.
   a. elegant   b. tranquil   c. tiresome

4. To _____ something is to soak it up.
   a. channel   b. suspend   c. absorb

5. At mealtimes, some families recite _____.
   a. grace   b. amateur   c. channel

6. Something that is _____ is peaceful and serene.
   a. elegant   b. lame   c. tranquil

7. To make a groove is to _____.
   a. channel   b. suspend   c. inspect

8. Someone who is _____ may not be able to move quickly.
   a. elegant   b. lame   c. tranquil

9. If you _____ an object, you look at it closely.
   a. absorb   b. grace   c. inspect

10. When something is high in quality, it is _____.
   a. elegant   b. lame   c. tiresome

The gown that the movie star wore on the red carpet was **elegant**.

Synonyms

*Choose the word that is most nearly the **same** in meaning as the word or phrase in **dark print**. Then write your choice on the line provided.*

1. boats in the **canal**

a. grace   b. amateur   c. channel   _____

2. scrutinize my face

a. inspect   b. absorb   c. suspend   _____

3. a **boring** task

a. elegant   b. tranquil   c. tiresome   _____

4. an **inadequate** excuse

a. lame   b. elegant   c. tranquil   _____

5. captivate my attention

a. grace   b. absorb   c. inspect   _____

Antonyms

*Choose the word that is most nearly **opposite** in meaning to the word or phrase in **dark print**. Then write your choice on the line provided.*

1. a **master** carpenter

a. channel   b. amateur   c. grace   _____

2. the **coarse** fabric

a. elegant   b. lame   c. tranquil   _____

3. a **noisy** place

a. tiresome   b. tranquil   c. lame   _____

4. extend the trip

a. absorb   b. inspect   c. suspend   _____

5. the comedian's **clumsiness**

a. amateur   b. channel   c. grace   _____

Completing the Sentence

Choose the word from the box that best completes each item below. Then write the word on the line provided. (You may have to change the word's ending.)

absorb	amateur	channel
elegant	grace	inspect
lame	suspend	
tiresome	tranquil	

Presidents

■ The life of the president of the United States is not a _____ one. It is full of activity and excitement.

■ Presidents must be hardworking. They have to _____ all their energy into their job.

■ Some duties of the office are _____. It may be tedious to

_____ all the papers that need to be signed, but that's one of the responsibilities of the president!

■ Franklin Delano Roosevelt, who was president from 1933 to 1945, was

made _____ by a disease called *polio*. He could not walk without braces.

■ George Washington had to _____ his life as a farmer to become president. He loved his farm in Virginia almost as much as his country.

First Ladies

■ The wives of American presidents are called *first ladies*. Most of the presidents' wives had experience in politics before

they came to the White House. They were not _____.

■ Jacqueline Kennedy, who was married to John F. Kennedy, was

considered _____ because she was beautiful and

stylish. She was famous for her charm and _____.

■ As first lady, Eleanor Roosevelt spoke out for the needs of the poor and

hungry. Her role as first lady _____ her full attention.

Both these women were important to our country.

Word Associations

Circle the letter next to the choice that best completes the sentence or answers the question. Pay special attention to the word in dark print.

1. Why do most **amateurs** in competition skate?
   a. because it is their job
   b. because they are experts
   c. to get rich
   d. just for the fun of it

2. To **inspect** a bicycle, you can
   a. check its tires and gears.
   b. read a bicycle magazine.
   c. glance at it quickly.
   d. lock it in the garage.

3. A **tiresome** task might make you
   a. burst into song.
   b. feel excited and happy.
   c. repeat it as soon as possible.
   d. complain of boredom.

4. To **suspend** a glass ornament,
   a. take a photo of it.
   b. sell it to a museum.
   c. hang it from your window.
   d. wrap it in soft padding.

5. Which animal runs with **grace**?
   a. a walrus
   b. a camel
   c. a turtle
   d. a deer

6. **Elegant** dinners often include
   a. paper plates and plastic forks.
   b. flowers, candles, and silverware.
   c. baby food and bottles.
   d. hot dogs and popcorn.

7. A **lame** research paper is probably
   a. a good one.
   b. a well-done one.
   c. a poor one.
   d. one you would like to hand in.

8. The English **Channel** is
   a. a television program.
   b. a wild party spot.
   c. a body of water.
   d. a city near London.

9. A **tranquil** scene is
   a. calm.
   b. noisy.
   c. busy.
   d. exciting.

10. If a book **absorbs** me, I
    a. put it back on the shelf.
    b. wipe it with a sponge.
    c. can't stop reading it.
    d. write my name in it.

Word Study • Suffixes -ion, -ment, -able

Remember that a **suffix** is a word part that is added to the end of a **base word** to make a new word.

Look at the base words and suffixes in this chart. The suffix -ion means "the act, state, or result of." You can add the suffix -ion to inspect (page 173) to make the word inspection. Inspection means "the act of inspecting."

The suffix -ment also means "the act, state, or result of." The suffix -able means "can be." Look at the chart for examples of words with the suffixes -ment and -able.

Base Word	Suffix	New Word	Meaning
inspect	+ **ion**	= inspec**tion**	→ act of inspecting
improve	+ **ment**	= improve**ment**	→ result of something improved
break	+ **able**	= break**able**	→ can be broken

PRACTICE *Write the missing base word or suffix. Then write the meaning of the new word.*

Base Word	Suffix	New Word	Meaning
1. connect	+ _____	= connection →	_____
2. enjoy	+ _____	= enjoyable →	_____
3. _____	+ ment	= agreement →	_____
4. respect	+ _____	= respectable →	_____

APPLY *Complete each sentence with words that contain the suffix -ion, -ment, or -able. Choose from the words in the boxes above.*

5. In order for the floor plan to pass _____, the town has to see

an _____ in the layout.

6. We made an _____ to handle the _____ glasses with care.

7. A story is more _____ when I make a _____ between the events in the story and my own life.

 Speak *Work with a partner. Add the suffix -ion to two of the base words and -ment to the other two. Use each new word in a sentence.*

subtract   measure   develop   protect

Shades of Meaning • Words That Describe Appearance

In the passage "The Nile Crocodile" on pages 170–171, you read this sentence: *Its **elegant** neck reaches down to the water*. The word *elegant* describes appearance, or how something looks. In the sentence, *elegant* tells what a gazelle's neck looks like. Look at the chart for other words that describe appearance.

elegant	Someone or something that is **elegant** looks beautiful and graceful.
shabby	When something or someplace looks **shabby**, it looks old and worn out.
tidy	Something or someplace that looks **tidy** is neat and orderly.

PRACTICE *Write the word from the chart that best completes each sentence.*

1. After we organized our books, the bookcase looked _____.

2. We wore old, _____ clothes when we painted the doghouse.

3. The movie star looked _____ in her long gown.

4. The cabin looked _____ because no one had lived there for a long time.

5. Our teacher always tells us to keep our desks _____.

6. The dining room looked _____ after it was decorated for the wedding.

APPLY *Write a sentence to describe how each place looks. Pay attention to the word in **dark print**. Use the word in your sentence.*

7. a **tidy** kitchen

_____

8. a **shabby** hotel

_____

9. an **elegant** restaurant

_____

Introducing the Words

Read the following textbook entry about a discovery that changed many lives. Notice how the highlighted words are used. These are the words you will be learning in this unit.

Gold! Gold! Gold!

(Textbook Entry)

Gold is the world's most valuable metal. One reason it is so valuable is because there is so little of it. What little there is can be hard to find. Still, many people have been willing to try to find it.

Hints of Gold in California

It was 1848 in California. Pieces of gold the size of peas glistened on the ground. James Marshall, a worker at a sawmill, picked them up. He told John Sutter, the mill owner, about his find. The two men agreed to keep it quiet. They didn't want to create an uproar that would bring people into the area to look for gold.

A storekeeper, Samuel Brannan, discovered their secret. He went to San Francisco, where he boasted about all the gold discovered at Sutter's Mill. At the same time, he invested the money he had. He bought items such as picks and shovels and got ready to sell them in a store near

John Sutter, owner
of Sutter's Mill

Sutter's Mill. It was an ideal plan: Miners would need supplies, and he would sell them everything they needed.

The Rush for Gold

What Marshall and Sutter had feared came true. The possibility of finding gold was sufficient encouragement for thousands of people. They sold their homes and left everything behind to search for gold. They came from all over the world. In all, more than eighty thousand people rushed to California.

Miners bent over streams day after day, looking for gold. They dipped metal pans into the rippling water and sifted for gold. They took tools called pickaxes and dug into the earth. The California Gold Rush was on!

Winners and Losers

Some people did become rich. Three German miners located a large supply of gold. Their mine eventually produced gold worth about $561 million today. Another small group, the Murphy brothers, found gold in their first few days of mining. By the end of the year, the gold they found was worth about $37 million in today's dollars.

Other people were not so lucky. Hiram Pierce came from Troy, New York. He paid $25 for a cradle, a tool that separated dirt from gold. By the time he returned home a year or two later, he was broke.

Pierce wrote eloquent descriptions and stories about mining. The work was difficult. Miners had to wade in freezing streams. They moved heavy dirt. They got hurt in accidents.

Many Native Americans were losers in the California Gold Rush, too. When miners became sick with infectious diseases, many Native Americans who lived in the area caught the diseases and died.

Today's Gold

Today, gold is used for many things. There is gold in some computer parts. People wear gold jewelry. Countries collect gold, which helps them protect the value of their money. As long as gold is scarce, it will continue to be the world's most precious metal.

Miners used a cradle to help them separate dirt from gold.

Gold nugget

Definitions

You were introduced to the words below in the passage on pages 180–181. Study the spelling, pronunciation, part of speech, and definition of each word. Write the word on the line in the sentence. Then read the synonyms and antonyms.

1. boast
(bōst)

(v.) to speak proudly of oneself, brag; to take pride in

The team members tend to _____ whenever they win.

(n.) talk that is too full of pride in oneself

My _____ about my grades drove away my friends.

SYNONYMS: (v.) crow, exaggerate, flaunt, overstate; (n.) self-praise
ANTONYM: (v.) belittle

2. eloquent
(el' ə kwənt)

(adj.) showing the ability to use words clearly and effectively

Martin Luther King, Jr., was an

_____ civil

rights speaker.

SYNONYMS: expressive, well-spoken, persuasive, forceful, powerful
ANTONYMS: awkward, tongue-tied

3. glisten
(gli' sən)

(v.) to shine with sparkling light

I like to see the morning dew _____ in the sunshine.

SYNONYMS: sparkle, glimmer, glitter, shimmer, gleam

4. ideal
(ī dēl')

(adj.) considered to be perfect; existing only in the imagination

Today was an _____ spring day.

(n.) a person or thing that is considered to be perfect

My _____ is a world without violence.

SYNONYMS: (adj.) supreme, flawless, exemplary, ultimate; (n.) model, example
ANTONYMS: (adj.) practical, pragmatic, real

5. infectious
(in fek′ shəs)

(adj.) caused or spread by germs; able or tending to spread from one to another

Chicken pox is a highly

_____ *disease.*

SYNONYMS: contagious, catching

6. invest
(in vest′)

(v.) to put money into something that will earn interest or make a profit; to make use of for future benefit

They will _____ *their money in stocks and bonds.*

SYNONYMS: spend, expend, contribute

7. locate
(lō′ kāt)

(v.) to find the position of; to settle into a place

I need to _____ *the highway on the map.*

SYNONYMS: discover, identify, pinpoint, detect, uncover; situate, build, establish

8. ripple
(rip′ əl)

(n.) a small wave

The pebble caused a _____ *in the pool.*

(v.) to form or cause small waves

A rowboat will _____ *the surface of the lake.*

SYNONYMS: (n.) vibration; (v.) ruffle, spread

9. sufficient
(sə fi′ shənt)

(adj.) as much as is needed, enough

We have a _____ *amount of time to finish our task.*

SYNONYMS: adequate, plenty, ample
ANTONYMS: insufficient, inadequate, deficient, lacking, sparse, scanty

10. uproar
(up′ rôr)

(n.) a state of noisy excitement, confusion

When I entered, I found the room in an _____.

SYNONYMS: disorder, commotion, disturbance
ANTONYMS: calmness, serenity, tranquility

Match the Meaning

vocabularyworkshop.com
Practice unit words with interactive games and activities.

Choose the word whose meaning is suggested by the clue given.
Then write the word on the line provided.

1. If you put money into something that will earn more money, you

_____ it.
  a. invest   b. ripple   c. boast

2. To brag is also to _____.
  a. glisten   b. locate   c. boast

3. When you find something, you _____ it.
  a. locate   b. invest   c. ripple

4. A well-spoken person can be described as

_____.
  a. ideal   b. infectious   c. eloquent

5. A(n) _____ is a small wave.
  a. uproar   b. ripple   c. boast

6. To have a(n)_____ amount is to
have as much as you need.
  a. eloquent   b. infectious   c. sufficient

7. A disease that can be caught by others is said to be

_____.
  a. infectious   b. sufficient   c. ideal

The campers used a map and a compass to locate the hidden treasure.

8. Something that is _____ is considered
to be perfect.
  a. eloquent   b. sufficient   c. ideal

9. If you cause a(n) _____, you create much excitement.
  a. uproar   b. boast   c. ripple

10. When an object shines, it might _____.
  a. locate   b. glisten   c. invest

Synonyms

*Choose the word that is most nearly the **same** in meaning as the word or phrase in **dark print**. Then write your choice on the line provided.*

1. a **contagious** laugh

    a. sufficient   b. infectious   c. eloquent   _____

2. created a **wave**

    a. ripple   b. uproar   c. boast   _____

3. shimmer in the moonlight

    a. boast   b. glisten   c. locate   _____

4. find your gloves

    a. invest   b. glisten   c. locate   _____

5. spend my time

    a. boast   b. ripple   c. invest   _____

6. an unnecessary **disturbance**

    a. ripple   b. uproar   c. boast   _____

Antonyms

*Choose the word that is most nearly **opposite** in meaning to the word or phrase in **dark print**. Then write your choice on the line provided.*

1. belittle oneself in front of others

    a. ripple   b. locate   c. boast about   _____

2. a **pragmatic** solution

    a. ideal   b. infectious   c. sufficient   _____

3. a **scanty** amount of food

    a. eloquent   b. infectious   c. sufficient   _____

4. a **fumbling** speech

    a. ideal   b. eloquent   c. infectious   _____

Completing the Sentence

Choose the word from the box that best completes each item below. Then write the word on the line provided. (You may have to change the word's ending.)

boast	eloquent	glisten
ideal	infectious	invest
locate	ripple	
sufficient	uproar	

Public Speaking

■ It is an art to be a good public speaker. The most _____ speakers know how to speak clearly and effectively.

■ The United States can _____ of many political leaders who were and are excellent communicators.

■ The moods and emotions of a speaker can be so

_____ that those same feelings are felt by the audience.

■ Sometimes, a speaker chooses to discuss a topic over which there are differences of opinion. At the end of a powerful speech that

addresses such a topic, the room might be in an _____.

■ When audiences enjoy a speaker, a _____ of applause often turns into thunderous applause.

Antoni Gaudí

■ Antoni Gaudí was a Spanish architect. He is known for the original and imaginative designs of his buildings. He found the

use of bright colors to be a(n) _____ way to make his buildings stand out.

■ My favorite Gaudí works are those that look like the scales of a dragon. I especially like looking at them when they

_____ in the sunshine.

■ Gaudí's most famous creation is La Sagrada Família, a church

_____ in Barcelona.

■ Gaudí _____ many years in this project, but it is still not finished after more than 100 years! It seems

there will never be _____ time to complete it!

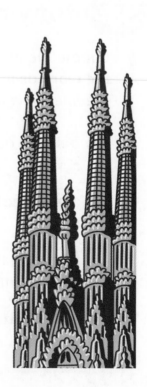

Word Study • Roots *loc, aud*

A **root** is the main part of a word. Roots have meaning, but few roots can stand alone. Sometimes, knowing the meaning of a root can help you figure out the meaning of a word.

The chart below gives the meanings of words with the roots *loc* and *aud*.

loc—place
The root **loc** appears in **locate** (page 183). When you **locate** something, you find its place.
aud—hear
The root **aud** appears in **audible**. When music is **audible**, you are able to hear it.

audience	a group of people gathered to see or hear something
auditorium	a large room or building where people gather to see and hear performances and other events
local	belonging or relating to a certain place, such as a town
location	a place or position

PRACTICE Complete each sentence with a word that contains the root *loc* or *aud*. Choose from the words above.

1. The car's radio was _____ from the sidewalk.

2. We had to _____ the park on a map.

3. We found a good _____ for our picnic.

4. The _____ was filled with people waiting for the show.

5. I buy _____ fruits because they are fresher.

6. The _____ cheered when the band came onto the stage.

APPLY Complete each sentence to show you understand the meaning of the word in **dark print**.

7. You might go to an **auditorium** to _____.

8. His voice was barely **audible** because _____.

9. A house might be hard to **locate** if _____.

Write Work with a partner to list other words that contain the roots *loc* and *aud*. Write definitions for the words. Then look in an online or classroom dictionary to check the meanings.

Vocabulary for Comprehension

*Read the following passage in which some of the words you have studied in Units 16–18 appear in **dark print**. Then answer the questions on page 189.*

Anansi the Hungry Spider

Anansi, a trickster, lived in a poor village where there was little food. Life there was **wretched** for all the animals, including spiders like Anansi.

A giant named Five also lived in the village. Everyone feared Five because she was mean and greedy. Those who spoke her name had to give her all the food they had. Thinking about Five helped hungry Anansi to conceive a plan. Soon he **negotiated** a deal with her. Anansi would help Five get food if she would share the prize with him. But he had to be careful *not* to say her name.

Anansi gathered **sufficient** corn to carry out the plan. He put the corn in five piles. Then, seated on one pile, he called to Rabbit, "Want some corn?" Of course, Rabbit did.

Anansi told him, "Count the piles, and one is yours!"

Rabbit counted, "One, two, three, four, five." As soon as the giant's name, Five, was said, poor Rabbit lost all his food. Anansi cooked the food and shared the feast with Five. For weeks, Anansi would **boast** about his feast.

When his food was no longer abundant, Anansi decided to trick Goose. Goose, however, didn't trust Anansi and **inspected** the situation carefully. As Anansi sat on a pile of corn, Goose counted. "One, two, three, four, …, and the one you're sitting on!"

Angry Anansi shouted, "That's wrong!"

Goose counted again. "One, two, three, four, …, and the one you're sitting on!"

By now, Anansi was in an **uproar**. He screamed, "No! It's one, two, three, four, five!" No sooner did Anansi say the word *five* than the giant seized all of Anansi's food. Goose smiled, said grace, and ate the corn. She not only tricked the trickster, she had…how many piles of corn?

Fill in the circle next to the choice that best completes the sentence or answers the question.

1. This passage is mostly about
   (a) a poor village.
   (b) how Anansi tries to trick the animals.
   (c) how Rabbit gets tricked.
   (d) how the giant tricked Anansi.

2. The meaning of **wretched** is
   (a) tricky.
   (b) greedy.
   (c) happy.
   (d) awful.

3. In this passage, **negotiated** means
   (a) discussed.
   (b) announced.
   (c) rejected.
   (d) dismissed.

4. **Sufficient** most nearly means
   (a) extra.
   (b) enough.
   (c) hardly any.
   (d) none.

5. The meaning of **boast** is
   (a) to complain.
   (b) to lose money.
   (c) to brag.
   (d) to act in a bashful way.

6. Another word for **inspected** is
   (a) examined.
   (b) ignored.
   (c) described.
   (d) modeled.

7. Goose outsmarted Anansi by
   (a) sharing her food with him.
   (b) counting slowly.
   (c) refusing to say the word *five*.
   (d) making her own deal with Five.

8. In this passage, **uproar** means
   (a) a feeling of calmness.
   (b) loud laughter.
   (c) a fight.
   (d) a state of excitement.

Write Your Own

In this story, Anansi learns that he can't fool everyone. Imagine how he felt after Goose tricked him and Five took all of his food. On a separate sheet of paper, write a journal entry from Anansi's point of view that describes how he felt. Use at least three words from Units 16–18.

Classifying

Choose the word from the box that goes best with each group of words. Write the word on the line provided. Then explain what the words have in common.

admirable   arch   channel
conceive   dreary   fearsome
formal   invest
purify   uproar

1. _____, lake, pond, river

_____

2. think, imagine, create, _____

_____

3. wall, roof, window, _____

_____

4. fear, fearful, fearless, _____

_____

5. comfortable, reasonable, _____, considerable

_____

6. save, spend, donate, _____

_____

7. eerie, leery, weary, _____

_____

8. earthquake, frostbite, headache, _____

_____

9. athletic, casual, dressy, _____

_____

10. freshen, filter, disinfect, _____

_____

Completing the Idea

Complete each sentence so that it makes sense. Pay attention to the word in **dark print**.

1. It was difficult to beat our **opponent** because_____.

2. I was awarded the **privilege** of _____.

3. My **ambition** for the future is to _____.

4. We had to **suspend** the game because _____.

5. An **eloquent** speaker might inspire people to _____.

6. Some scientists try to **predict** _____.

7. A referee will **penalize** a player who _____.

8. A **modest** person would not _____.

9. One chore that is **tiresome** is _____.

10. My uncle asked me to **locate** _____.

11. I often **yearn** for _____.

12. When I visit the museum, I want to **inquire** about _____.

13. You can **merit** an allowance by _____.

14. I try to **absorb** new information by _____.

15. The **ideal** time to go for a jog is _____.

Writing Challenge

Write two sentences using the word **stunt**. In the first sentence, use **stunt** as a verb. In the second sentence, use **stunt** as a noun.

1. _____

2. _____

Index